The Open University

Science Short Course

# Molecules, medicines and drugs: a chemical story

Bob Allgrove and Peter Morrod

# The SK185 Course Team

| | |
|---|---|
| Peter Morrod | *Chair and Author* |
| Bob Allgrove | *Author* |
| Christine Heading | *Critical Reader* |
| Fiona Aiken | *Critical Reader* |
| Isla McTaggart | *Course Manager* |
| Jenny Hudson | *Course Team Assistant* |
| Bina Sharma | *Media Developer* |
| Sara Hack | *Media Developer* |
| Steve Best | *Media Developer* |
| Sarah Hofton | *Media Developer* |
| Neil Paterson | *Media Assistant* |
| Rafael Hidalgo | *Media Project Manager* |
| Martin Keeling | *Rights Executive* |
| Jane Henley | *Indexer* |
| Sabbir Ahmed | *Course Assessor, University of Kingston* |

Much of the material in this book was edited from the now discontinued course ST240 *Our Chemical Environment*, and the contribution of the ST240 Course Team is gratefully acknowledged.

This publication forms part of an Open University course SK185 *Molecules, medicines and drugs: a chemical story*. Details of this and other Open University courses can be obtained from the Student Registration and Enquiry Service, The Open University, PO Box 197, Milton Keynes MK7 6BJ, United Kingdom: tel. +44 (0)845 300 60 90, email general-enquiries@open.ac.uk

Alternatively, you may visit the Open University website at http://www.open.ac.uk where you can learn more about the wide range of courses and packs offered at all levels by The Open University.

To purchase a selection of Open University course materials visit http://www.ouw.co.uk, or contact Open University Worldwide, Michael Young Building, Walton Hall, Milton Keynes MK7 6AA, United Kingdom for a brochure: tel. +44 (0)1908 858793; fax +44 (0)1908 858787; email ouw-customer-services@open.ac.uk

The Open University
Walton Hall, Milton Keynes
MK7 6AA

First published 2006. Second edition 2007.

Copyright © 2006, 2007 The Open University

Edited and designed by The Open University.

Typeset by The Open University.

Printed and bound in the United Kingdom by The University Press, Cambridge.

ISBN 978 0 7492 2683 1

2.1

# Contents

**Important note from the SK185 Course Team**

SK185 teaches some of the science behind drug discovery and development, not the suitability of treatments in specific cases. It is important to follow appropriate medical advice and never to use SK185 material to make decisions about suitable treatment for individual illnesses or conditions.

# What's behind it all?

If you asked ten different people to suggest technological inventions and discoveries that have proved to be of great benefit to humans, you would almost certainly get ten different lists. However, anyone who can remember having an abscess under a tooth may well have a number of drug discoveries well to the fore in their list. Although it might be difficult to rank them in order of importance, it is likely that drugs to control the pain immediately, antibiotics to eliminate the bacterial infection and local anaesthetics for use when the tooth is extracted or root-filled can all be regarded as important in that person's life at particular times. To this list could be added the bactericidal mouthwash used in the dentist's surgery to reduce the chance of infection being transmitted.

On the other hand, if you have asthma, or know someone who does, you are perhaps likely to have placed drugs that are able to control symptoms, albeit without affecting a cure, quite high up on your list.

*Molecules, medicines and drugs: a chemical story* attempts to describe aspects of the uniquely human activity of seeking cures and preventions for the diseases with which our species is afflicted. We start by considering the social context of drug development and then move on to the science behind the mode of action of a variety of medicinal drugs (Figure 1.1). The chemical principles needed to understand how these drugs work will be explained. At times you will find that the course adopts a somewhat historical flavour – there are some fascinating stories behind the discovery of such common drugs as aspirin and the antibacterials sulfonamide* and penicillin. The course finishes with a look at what the future may hold, including potential treatment for avian flu and AIDS.

Let's begin by exploring some of the interrelationships between drug research and society.

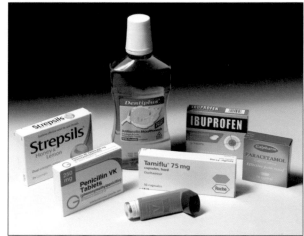

**Figure 1.1** Some of the medicines that will be discussed in this course.

## 1.1 Medicinal drugs and society

As a society develops it is able to devote its attention to more areas of activity. If one considers the needs of a social group early in the evolution of humans it does not take much thought to arrive at the conclusion that the most important needs are for air, drinking water and food. Without these people cannot survive, so the society cannot develop. In places such as the UK people tend to take these things for granted. There is plenty of clean air, safe drinking water is piped to every home and an abundance of food is heaped up in supermarkets.

---

* Note the spelling of the name of the yellow, solid element sulfur (sulphur). In 1992 The Royal Society of Chemistry adopted the international agreement that it is spelled with an 'f' rather than 'ph'. So this style spills over into the names of chemicals derived from sulfur, such as sulfuric acid and sulfonamides. If you do a web search, you can find some interesting history associated with the etymology (Old English: *seolfor*, Middle English: *sulfre*, Latin: *sulfur*).

It is interesting to reflect on what happens when the availability of any of these is temporarily threatened, though. In the UK, the 'peasouper' fogs in the 1950s led to a high number of fatalities. The government responded by introducing legislation to clean up the air by making changes to human activities; for example, coal fires were banned in many centres of high population. More recently, there has been increasingly strict control of the permitted levels of exhaust emissions by motor vehicles, with regular compulsory testing to ensure compliance. Any contamination of the drinking water supply is treated as a top-priority emergency and even a relatively minor and isolated problem is likely to feature in national news bulletins. Similarly, any threat to the safety of the food supply, say bacterially contaminated meat on sale in a butcher's shop, is likely to have severe consequences, even imprisonment, for those responsible. Society is quick to respond when its basic needs are threatened!

Close behind air to breathe, water to drink and food to eat comes the need for shelter and warmth, unless the climate is particularly favourable. Once these are satisfied, a civilisation can start to give attention to creative activities, such as the arts and education, and become inquisitive about its environment beyond just the needs for survival. A long way down this route one finds that a society is able to devote the effort needed to develop chemical and medical understanding to the level that many people enjoy today. Not that humans are anywhere near the utopia that we would like to be. Although many diseases have been eradicated there are many more that have not and evolution sees to it that new diseases (e.g. MRSA (Box 1.1), AIDS and avian flu) appear from time to time.

### Box 1.1  MRSA

*Staphylococcus aureus* is a bacterium that lives harmlessly on the skin or in the nose of about one-third of healthy people. It causes infection if it enters the body via damaged skin but can be readily treated with antibiotics, such as methicillin, if the need arises. MRSA (methicillin-resistant *Staphylococcus aureus*) is a variant that first appeared in the 1960s with new, more virulent strains of the bacterium appearing in the 1980s and 1990s. Its name reflects the fact that it does not respond to methicillin.

MRSA infections can be found in hospital patients, and are often caused by the transfer of bacteria to patients' skin by contact with other people or equipment. In an attempt to prevent infection with MRSA, hospitals have adopted increasingly more stringent hygiene procedures.

● List some possible reasons for the increased incidence of MRSA in hospitals since the 1990s. You may find it useful to discuss this with someone else.

● The following is not an exhaustive list and you may have thought of additional reasons. Possibilities are:

  • New strains are more virulent so are more easily spread by hands and equipment.

  • There may be an increased number of elderly or very ill patients in hospitals who will be more susceptible to infection.

- Patient transfer between and within hospitals may have become more common and so facilitate the spread of bacterial infection.
- Medical procedures may have become more complex, thus increasing the number of health care workers with whom the patient comes into contact.
- Although the appearance of MRSA has resulted in increasingly strict hygiene procedures, e.g. hand washing before and after attending to a patient, the increased workload of health care workers could result in reduced compliance.

Perhaps western society has not yet developed to the stage where it is able to devote sufficient resources to advance the science of curing and avoiding diseases at the speed that it would like. In the following sections you will look at some of the factors involved in the discovery and development of medicinal drugs.

If you picture, in your mind's eye, people developing drugs you will almost certainly have clad them in white coats and placed them in laboratories surrounded by various bottles of chemicals, complicated-looking apparatus and computers (Figure 1.2).

These people are, however, in a minority when you look at the broader spectrum of what is taking place. There are many more people involved in providing the funding for the scientists' work. Anyone who has a bank account or some other form of investment is involved; as is anyone who buys a product made by one of the drug manufacturers. Alternatively, some of the research may be funded by governments, through taxation. Either way, it is you, me and lots of other people, all connected to the availability of funding, that make medicinal drug development possible. Without an annual worldwide investment of many billions of pounds, the people in white coats would soon find their work curtailed. And here is the problem. People generally do not want to spend all of their spare money on finding new medicinal drugs for curing their ailments. They also want to have holidays and televisions, buy better houses, fly people into space and so on – the list is endless. So, perhaps satisfying their other needs has not yet reached the stage where people can concentrate on improving their existence to the point where remaining diseases could possibly be eradicated or controlled.

'That's Dr Arnold Moore. He's conducting an experiment to test the theory that most great scientific discoveries were hit on by accident.'

**Figure 1.2** Research in progress …

## 1.2 A general strategy for drug discovery

Many drugs have been developed from products with useful properties that occur naturally in plants or animals. They may have been known about and used for a very long time, without any understanding of how they achieve their effects. For example, the Incas are known to have chewed leaves of *Erythroxylum coca* (coca leaves), which produced a numbing effect on the tongue, probably as long ago as 500 BC. If you were given the task of making a local anaesthetic when none was available, the task would be daunting but, armed with a naturally occurring compound that could be extracted from coca leaves, it would get a lot simpler.

Such a compound is known as a 'lead compound' (used in the sense of leading the way, so rhymes with *bleed* rather than *bled*). You will explore the coca story in detail in Chapter 4, but for now take a look at the typical sequence of events that results in a useful drug being developed from a potentially hopeful lead compound.

Figure 1.3 illustrates how chemical knowledge is important in the discovery and development of a new drug. If the lead compound is contained within a naturally occurring material it is likely that something is already known about its biological activity. However, before any useful work can be done it is necessary to extract the active ingredient and identify exactly what it is. The extraction stage (step 1) may not be too difficult – we extract caffeine from tea leaves whenever we make a cup of tea simply by pouring boiling water on the leaves. The caffeine dissolves in the

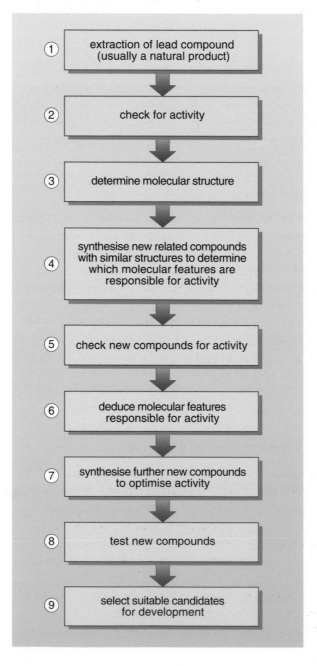

**Figure 1.3**   The nine steps in a strategy for drug discovery.

water, from which it can be isolated by stirring the solution of caffeine in water with another liquid (solvent) that does not mix with water but does dissolve caffeine. If the new solution is separated from the water, the caffeine can be obtained by evaporating the solvent, leaving a residue of impure caffeine.

After checking the activity of the compound (step 2), the next step (step 3) is to determine its molecular structure. This could, in the past, take many years if the structure was complicated. For example, Frederick Sanger worked on the analysis of insulin at Cambridge University for eight years before he was finally able to declare the amino acid sequence (see Chapter 3) in its structure in 1953. His work was recognised by the award of the Nobel Prize in Chemistry in 1958. Things have speeded up in more recent times as modern analytical techniques have become available. However, the elucidation of the structure of a complicated biochemical molecule can still be a daunting task and would be even more so without the help of computers to deal with masses of information quickly and accurately.

Once the structure of the lead compound is known, new related compounds can be synthesised (step 4) by changing the molecular structure systematically, a bit at a time, to find out which parts of it are essential to its activity and which parts of it can be modified to improve it. The improvements can come in many forms, for example the modified compound may be more active, have reduced side-effects or be longer lasting. In Chapter 6 you will look at the development of drugs to control the symptoms of asthma, by progressive modification of the structure of the active ingredient in an ancient Chinese herbal remedy (*ma huang*), to give us the modern asthma relief drug, salbutamol.

In many ways the latter stages in the strategy for drug discovery (steps 5–7) repeat the earlier ones. Once a new candidate has been prepared by modifying the chemical structure of the lead compound it can be tested for activity, further modified and so on. Even when a suitable candidate has been selected, this potential drug requires development by pre-clinical and clinical testing (step 8) before the final drug is marketed (step 9). It is hardly surprising, then, that the process is slow and expensive. Nor should it come as much of a surprise to find that the later part of this chapter looks at some basic ideas underlying chemical structures – the different ways that atoms can bond together to form molecules of compounds with some very different properties.

## 1.3 Drug testing

This section focuses on step 8 in the strategy outlined in Figure 1.3.

Back in the 19th century, when chemical research was in its infancy, one of the common tests carried out by researchers on new, hitherto unknown, potential drugs was to eat them and see what happened, or give them to someone else to eat. Nowadays, this practice would be strongly discouraged; society takes a more responsible attitude towards the health and safety of employees. However, this practice did meet with some success; see the development of aspirin in Chapter 2, tested by the discoverer, Felix Hoffmann, on his father who had rheumatism! Nowadays, every new drug that reaches the market is the result of many years of painstaking research and development before large scale manufacture can be undertaken, with almost all the initially hopeful compounds failing to progress beyond one step or another.

An example of the potential consequences of not carrying out rigorous and painstaking testing was the disastrous result of the use of thalidomide, a sedative drug that was used to suppress morning sickness during pregnancy in the late 1950s and early 1960s. At that time the testing programmes in Europe were far less stringent than they are now and the drug worked well to alleviate the discomfort of morning sickness. What was not fully understood at the time is that thalidomide restricts blood flow. The symptoms of morning sickness are often at their height at around the time that the foetus is developing limb growth. The result was that restricted blood flow reduced pre-natal limb growth, leading to the birth of many thousands of babies with severely shortened limbs.

The drug testing programmes in the USA were already much more rigorous than in Europe so thalidomide had not been passed for use by the US Food and Drug Administration (FDA). The result was that the disastrous news emanating from Europe prevented the use of thalidomide in the USA and very few cases of thalidomide-induced deformities were reported there. Of the few that were, it was suggested that they were probably caused by thalidomide that had been used elsewhere or taken into the country unofficially.

More recent work has revealed that thalidomide may well be useful for treating disorders where the reduction of blood flow can be beneficial, for example for the alleviation of the symptoms of some forms of leprosy and for the suppression of some forms of cancerous growths.

It is the testing process that is the most expensive and time-consuming and research programmes can be abandoned at any stage if the cost–benefit analysis becomes unfavourable. The first stage of testing involves two studies on at least two non-human animal species for two reasons: (a) to determine the toxic effect of high single doses and (b) to investigate the longer term effect of varied and repeated doses. A typical programme at this pre-clinical stage could take around a year, before testing on humans takes place.

Once the pre-clinical stage is satisfactorily over, clinical trials may be commenced on humans, under medical supervision. These can be divided into three stages. The first involves testing how well the product is tolerated by healthy volunteers, in single and repeated doses. This may take another year and is not without risk to the volunteers.

The next stage, another year or two here, involves testing the drug for efficacy (does it work?) and safety on selected patients known to have the condition the drug is intended for. It is in this stage that appropriate formulations are selected for use in the next stages. Formulation involves processing the drug into a suitable form (e.g. tablet, capsule, injection) for administering to a patient. Once in this form it has become a medicine. For simplicity this course will use the term 'drug' to include unformulated and formulated drugs (medicines) as well. It will only specifically refer to medicines if there is some special point to make.

This efficacy testing is followed by the final stage in drug testing. First the cost–benefit analysis is updated, based on the information from the earlier stages. If the chance of a successful and profitable launch outweighs the risk, large-scale trials will be carried out on several thousand patients. If the analysis reveals that the drug is unlikely to be profitable, further trials are unlikely because this final stage is the most expensive stage in the process. Assuming the forecast is favourable, the important thing in this last stage of the trials is to ensure that the results of the research are genuine and not affected by any preconceived attitudes of the patients, the researchers or the health care workers. Strict statistical control of the experiment is therefore needed, with some patients being given a placebo (a non-active 'look alike' to the drug) rather than the drug itself, to see if it really is the drug that may be having an effect or just the expectation that it will. Likewise, the health care workers who are administrating the experimental treatment are likely to be unaware of whether they are giving the drug or a placebo to a particular patient. This is known as a double-blind experiment and is designed to remove the possibility of bias in the results arising from expected, or hoped for, outcomes. For further comparison, some of the patients may be given an established drug rather than the experimental one or the placebo. This stage can take up to around two years.

One result of long testing programmes is that new drugs are usually expensive. Pharmaceutical companies need to recover the enormous cost of developing the drug and then make a profit by selling it. Given exclusive patent rights lasting 20 years, if it takes 12 years from initial discovery to get a drug approved and generally available on the market, there are only eight years left for the company to recover its research and development costs and make a profit before the patent expires and other companies start making the drug and selling it more cheaply. A lot of the profit will need to be fed back into the company to develop the next new drug. One result of this process is that not everyone can afford to pay for the newest and potentially best drugs to treat a given condition. Tensions build up as some patients are offered the newer drugs, whilst others have to be content with drugs which have been available for longer and are therefore cheaper, but still profitable, because their development costs have already been recovered.

If you want to follow up drugs testing in more detail, and for some specific drugs, you could do a web search. Try 'new drugs tests' followed by the name of one of the pharmaceutical companies, e.g. Pfizer, GlaxoSmithKline or Bayer. You should be able to find information about the procedures adopted. Some of the information is dealt with at a research level, so you will find some web pages go well beyond the scope of this course. Three stages of clinical testing were described here. You could see if your searches identify a fourth stage and, if so, what it achieves.

As the development, manufacture and mode of action of drugs are firmly based in chemistry, we will now introduce some essential chemical ideas that underpin much of the work in later chapters. Please work carefully through the rest of Chapter 1, including the use of the model kit, as it will facilitate your understanding of the rest of the course.

Before you move on, however, you might like to listen to the three radio programmes *Quest for a Cure I–III* on CD1 and 2. The discussion focuses on the background to the attempts to develop an anti-AIDS drug, maraviroc, at Pfizer's laboratories in Sandwich, Kent. The programmes tell a fascinating story and you will recognise many of the topics we have discussed so far, in particular the high costs involved and high failure rate in drug research and development.

Maraviroc is, at the time of writing (August 2006), in its final stage of clinical testing. If all goes well it could be expected to receive approval for use sometime in 2007 or 2008, around 20 years after Pfizer started the quest for it. You could try a web search – just enter 'maraviroc' – to follow its progress.

## 1.4   Some ideas about chemical structures

An element is a chemical, a material that cannot be separated into simpler chemicals (but see later in Section 1.7.2 for a more quantitative definition). The smallest part of an element that can exist is an atom. You have already come across the element sulfur. It can be made into lots of other chemicals, called compounds, by combining it with other elements but it cannot be divided by any known means into other elements that are simpler than sulfur. Now we have also introduced the term compound and, by implication defined it as a material that contains more than one element. The only additional thing to note at this stage is that in a compound the constituent elements are not just mixed together, but are somehow bound together in a way that makes them rather difficult to separate. This is the essential difference between a compound and a mixture. It follows, then, that the forces between the components of a mixture should be found to be weaker than the forces between the atoms in a compound.

As there are more than 100 elements, the prospect of looking at how and why they all combine with each other could be rather daunting! However, luck is on our side here and there is only a very limited number of different elements whose atoms are involved in making the molecules that we are interested in. An atom is the smallest part of an element that can exist and still be that element, and a molecule is the smallest part of a compound that can exist and still be that compound.

 Now unpack your molecular model kit. You should find six kinds of colour-coded balls. These can be used to represent atoms of the five elements that occur most often in biological molecules and in drugs. You should also find coloured plastic 'sticks'. There are two kinds, short and long. You will need the long ones later, but for the present just use the short ones. These 'sticks' are used to represent the bonds that can form between atoms of elements, holding them together in molecules. The two green balls will not be used to represent atoms of a specific element but instead they will be used when we need to represent a non-specific atom or group of atoms.

If you examine the balls you will find holes into which the bonds can be pushed. When the models are new the bonds can be a rather tight fit but they do soon loosen up with use. Using a pair of pliers to hold each bond can help; you may also find it helpful to wiggle the bonds when connecting or disconnecting them. Now compare the atoms of the different elements and look for the differences and similarities. Columns 1 and 2 of Table 1.1 summarise what you should have found.

**Table 1.1**   The common elements of biological molecules. (Colour and number of holes refer to the ball in the model kit that is used to represent that element.)

| Colour | Number of holes | Name of element | Symbol for element | Valency |
| --- | --- | --- | --- | --- |
| white | 1 | hydrogen | H | 1 |
| black | 4 | carbon | C | 4 |
| red | 2 | oxygen | O | 2 |
| blue | 4 | nitrogen | N | 3 or 4 |
| yellow | 2 | sulfur | S | 2 usually |

Strictly speaking, the symbol for each element means one atom of that element and is useful when writing the chemical formulae of compounds. You may also find the symbol sometimes used just to mean the element, though. Note the word valency in Table 1.1. The valency of an element in a compound is the number of bonds that each atom of it has formed. This is simple enough for hydrogen, carbon and oxygen as they each can have only one valency value. It is a bit more awkward with nitrogen as the atom can form three or four bonds with equal ease; this will be explained when the need arises. Similarly, sulfur often has a valency of two, but it can be four or six, so sulfur atoms with four and six holes can also be found in some model kits.

The reason for the very specific value(s) of the valencies of each element will not be explained here, as it requires a study of theoretical chemistry and physics that would not contribute anything to the main ideas in the course – how drugs work.

### Activity 1.1

Rather than breaking them up each time you may find it useful to keep the models you make for later use.

1    Take a carbon atom, four hydrogen atoms and four of the short bonds from your kit and join them all together to form a single molecule. There is only one way of doing this and the result is a model of a molecule of methane, the fossil fuel gas that many of us burn to heat our houses. It is also the simplest possible hydrocarbon, a name derived from the fact that it contains *only* the elements hydrogen and carbon.

2    Now make another model, this time with two carbon atoms and six hydrogen atoms. You will need seven bonds this time and, again, there is only one way that the atoms can be joined. You have made a model of a molecule of ethane.

3    Compare your models to ours shown in Figure 1.4.

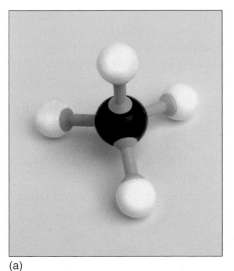

(a)

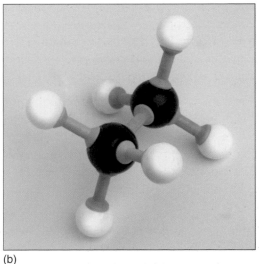

(b)

**Figure 1.4**   Models of (a) methane and (b) ethane.

4    Repeat 2, but with three carbon atoms – this time you decide how many hydrogen atoms and bonds you need. The rule is that each of the carbons must have four bonds joined to it and each hydrogen must have one bond – remember the idea of valency from Table 1.1. You have made a molecule of propane, a gas that is often found in the 'bottled gas' used for appliances such as camping stoves.

Now let's see how the structures of these molecules can be written in chemical shorthand. Write down the formula of each of the molecules you have made in the style $C_xH_y$, where $x$ = the number of carbon atoms and $y$ = the number of hydrogen atoms in one molecule. Can you spot a pattern in the values of $x$ and $y$ for the three compounds?

You should have ended up with $CH_4$, $C_2H_6$ and $C_3H_8$. (By convention if there is only one atom of an element in a molecule the '1' is taken as read, so methane is $CH_4$ rather than $C_1H_4$, although the latter is not wrong and chemists would recognise its meaning even though they would think it looks a bit strange.) This style of writing a formula is known as the molecular formula. You may have spotted that each formula differs from the previous one by an increment of $-CH_2-$ . Such a series of compounds is known as a homologous series and the members of the series are homologues of each other. The names given to your three compounds are methane, ethane and propane.

5    Now try making a molecule with four carbon atoms and the appropriate number of hydrogen atoms and bonds. Did you find something different about doing this, compared with 1, 2 and 3?

You should have found some indecision here, because there are two different ways of joining together four carbon atoms. Your carbon chain could have been unbranched or branched. Try making both versions. You should find you need ten hydrogen atoms for each version of the molecule. In the unbranched structure each carbon atom is joined to only one or two other carbon atoms (Figure 1.5a). The branched structure has one carbon atom joined to three other carbon atoms (Figure 1.5b). The unbranched structure is butane. The two structures enjoy a special relationship because they have the same molecular formula ($C_4H_{10}$) but are different compounds. They are known as isomers of each other (from Greek *isos*, the same; *meros*, parts). For this reason one name used for the branched structure is isobutane, but it is more commonly referred to by its systematic name, methylpropane. In this style of naming the longest unbranched carbon chain is found and named as if the side-chain was absent (propane) and then the side-chain is named. The name of the side-chain is derived from the hydrocarbon with the same number of carbon atoms as the side-chain by changing –ane to –yl. So, methane gives us the methyl group, a group of atoms that, as you will see, is very common in organic molecules. Like propane, these two isomers are also present in 'bottled gas'.

You could keep your molecular model of butane; you will need it again later in this chapter.

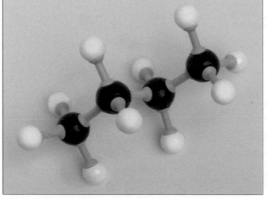
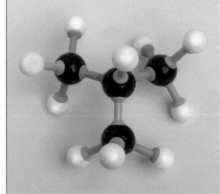

**Figure 1.5**    Models of (a) butane and (b) methylpropane.

(a)                                                                                (b)

## 1.5  Depicting chemical structures

For chemists to be able to read, write and communicate, some way of writing down chemical structures is needed. Pictures of ball-and-stick models are quite useful, provided they are simple, otherwise drawing three-dimensional objects on two-dimensional paper becomes complicated. So, methane and ethane are immediately recognisable in Figure 1.4. Looking at bigger molecules, by the time you get to butane and methylpropane the structures are getting quite complicated (Figure 1.5), but are still recognisable.

Imagine the problem of trying to draw, or photograph a molecular model of carotene ($C_{40}H_{56}$) which occurs in carrots and is a source of vitamin A. Although carotene is really just another hydrocarbon, so the model only needs two kinds of atom, you have not been asked to make it – you probably wouldn't anyway, even if you had been given enough atoms!

So, we need a simpler way of depicting structures. In Figure 1.6 there are two other ways of showing each of butane (a) and methylpropane (b). Note, though, that we have lost some of the detail of the three-dimensional representations. This does not matter if the three-dimensional shape is not important for whatever is under consideration, so the styles in Figure 1.6 can be quite useful. Both of the structures shown in (a) are common representations of the butane molecule, and both of those shown in (b) are equally valid for methylpropane.

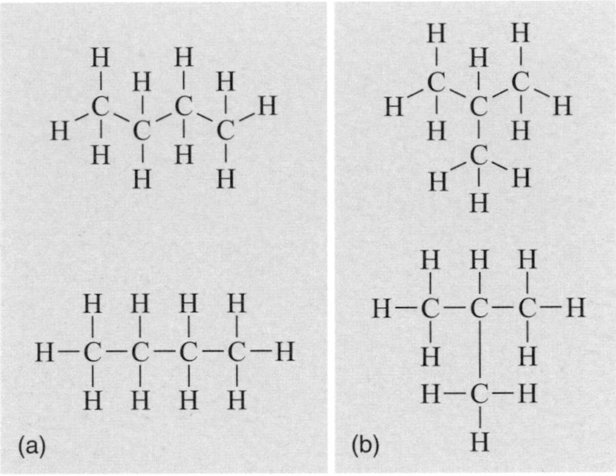

Once it is realised that each hydrogen atom must be joined to a carbon atom with a bond and there must be four bonds to each carbon, but only one to each hydrogen, it becomes a simple matter to reduce the complexity of the diagrams of the structure still further. Have a look at Figure 1.7 and you should see that the styles shown are unambiguous representations of the structure of butane. Compare these representations with those in Figure 1.6a. Although some of the bonds in Figure 1.7a and b do appear to point towards hydrogen atoms, they join to the carbon atoms with the bonds to the hydrogen atoms omitted. You could just do a quick check that all the valencies are correct.

**Figure 1.6**  Some full structural formulae: (a) 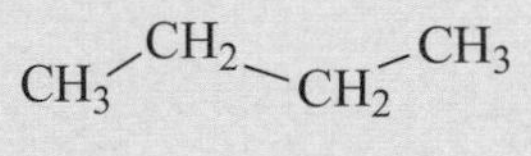 butane; (b) methylpropane.

**Figure 1.7**  Some condensed structural formulae of butane.

Figure 1.7c is the simplest style and is often used as it is easier and quicker to write (especially on a word processor!) than the styles that show all or even some of the bonds. To the inexperienced eye it does not convey the same amount of information that the more explicit styles in (a) and (b) do, but with a bit of experience a chemist looking at $CH_3CH_2CH_2CH_3$ can immediately visualise a more detailed structure having all the bonds and atoms shown separately.

Now have a look at the structures in Figure 1.8. You should find it easy enough to visualise each compound's structure in the various other styles that have been discussed – if not, try making a model of one of them. You have already seen the first four compounds. All these compounds occur naturally, in petroleum. You may recognise the name octane in connection with motor fuel – it is one of the major constituents of ordinary petrol. All these compounds contain only the elements hydrogen and carbon, and as you know are called hydrocarbons. They are part of the homologous series known as the alkanes.

| | |
|---|---|
| methane | $CH_4$ |
| ethane | $CH_3CH_3$ |
| propane | $CH_3CH_2CH_3$ |
| butane | $CH_3CH_2CH_2CH_3$ |
| pentane | $CH_3CH_2CH_2CH_2CH_3$ |
| hexane | $CH_3CH_2CH_2CH_2CH_2CH_3$ |
| heptane | $CH_3CH_2CH_2CH_2CH_2CH_2CH_3$ |
| octane | $CH_3CH_2CH_2CH_2CH_2CH_2CH_2CH_3$ |

**Figure 1.8**   The first eight members of the alkane series.

Octane looks to be a fairly big molecule but, once you realise that each member of a homologous series differs only by a unit of $-CH_2-$ from the previous one, it becomes apparent that there is no theoretical limit to how big an alkane molecule can be. Polythene, the familiar plastic used to make so many common things, contains alkane molecules with many thousands of $-CH_2-$ units in each molecule.

## 1.6   An aside – some further ideas about models and modelling

Before looking at the chemistry of drugs and how they interact with their targets some more detail on chemical bonding is needed. This will be provided by the use of some more modelling ideas but, first, let's just think a bit about exactly what is meant by the term *model*.

Suppose you were asked to draw a picture of a model of a human. The first thing you need to know is what exactly is supposed to be depicted by the model. So, for example, if the model was to be used to discuss and illustrate the function of a human as a food processor it might be sufficient to show a model existing as two parallel straight lines (Figure 1.9a) to represent a tube. Food can enter at the top, be processed and exit at the bottom.

On the other hand, if the model was supposed to illustrate how a human can be used to hang clothes on, the simple model of the gut drawn above would be totally useless. Something like Figure 1.9b would be much more useful.

Neither Figure 1.9a nor 1.9b *looks* much like a human, but we could choose which one we are going to use to deal with a particular aspect of human

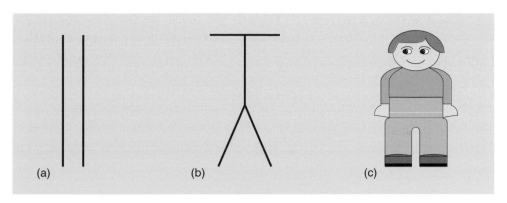

**Figure 1.9** Models of a 'human'.

properties. The first would be useless if we wanted to look at the design of clothes, whilst the second would be hopeless for any work on the digestive system. Figure 1.9c looks more like a human but would be pretty useless for both tasks.

In general, a model enables you to focus on one particular aspect of something, ignoring anything that you are not interested in. Models are therefore always lacking in some detail or other. The advance of chemical knowledge is a fascinating story of the development of ever more refined models that are designed to represent how chemists think they can account for how materials behave. We have come a long way since the Greek philosophers, Lueccipus and Democritus in the 5th century BC suggested that all matter is composed of the four elements earth, air, fire and water. Although modern thinking finds this suggestion ludicrous, it was not without experimental basis. Whenever something is burned it clearly gives fire. If a cool surface is held above the flame water condenses on it. Gases ('air') are given off in the burning process and can be felt in the updraft from a fire and there is a residue of ash ('earth'). So, it was argued, these four things must have been present in the original material and, since no other products are detected, these four things must be the elements from which all matter is composed.

● Now return to your ball-and-stick model of methane and try to think what it is depicting that could be true for a real molecule of methane.

● This is almost impossible because no-one has ever seen a molecule of methane – it is far too small. It is unlikely that the carbon atom is black, the hydrogen atoms are white and the bonds are grey, so we could probably discard those aspects of the model as irrelevant. However, we would expect the number of each type of atom in the molecule to be correct and possibly the overall shape of the molecule too.

Detailed work in chemistry and physics does confirm two things about methane that are also true for the model: (a) each atom can be rotated about the bonds that join to it and (b) all the angles between adjacent bonds are the same size. This angle is close to 109.5° giving the molecule the overall shape of a tetrahedron, a four-sided solid with each of the faces being an equilateral triangle*. The carbon atom is at the centre of the solid and a hydrogen atom is at each corner. The angle of 109.5° is often called the tetrahedral angle and methane is described as a tetrahedral molecule.

---

* In an equilateral triangle all three sides are the same length.

### Activity 1.2

Use models of the structures of butane and methylpropane to decide which of A, B, C and D, shown in Figure 1.10, are butane and which are methylpropane. You will need to use the principle of superimposability – identical things such as our models can be superimposed exactly on each other, either physically or in the imagination. You will also need to use the idea that atoms and groups of atoms can rotate about the bonds that join them.

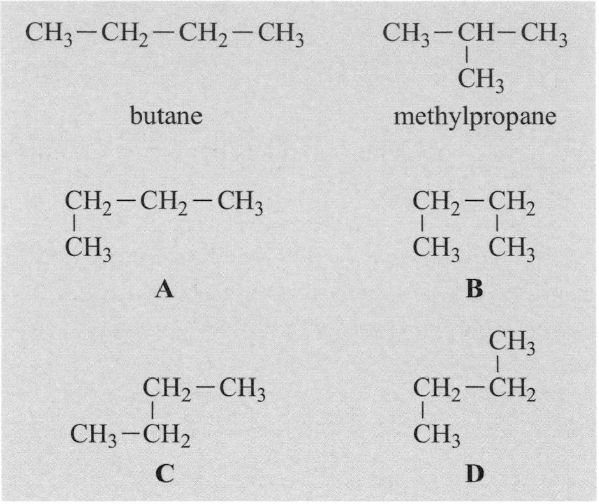

$$CH_3 - CH_2 - CH_2 - CH_3 \qquad\qquad CH_3 - CH - CH_3$$
$$\qquad\qquad\qquad\qquad\qquad\qquad | $$
$$\qquad\qquad\qquad\qquad\qquad\qquad CH_3$$

butane                                  methylpropane

$$CH_2 - CH_2 - CH_3 \qquad\qquad CH_2 - CH_2$$
$$| \qquad\qquad\qquad\qquad\qquad\qquad | \qquad\quad |$$
$$CH_3 \qquad\qquad\qquad\qquad\qquad CH_3 \quad CH_3$$

**A**                                         **B**

$$\qquad\qquad\qquad\qquad\qquad\qquad\qquad\qquad CH_3$$
$$\qquad\qquad\qquad\qquad\qquad\qquad\qquad\qquad |$$
$$CH_2 - CH_3 \qquad\qquad CH_2 - CH_2$$
$$| \qquad\qquad\qquad\qquad\qquad\qquad |$$
$$CH_3 - CH_2 \qquad\qquad\qquad CH_3$$

**C**                                         **D**

**Figure 1.10**   Structural formulae for $C_4H_{10}$.

You should have concluded that A, B, C and D are all models of butane. If you do not agree, go back to the ball-and-stick model for butane and show that it can be converted into any one of A, B, C or D simply by rotation of atoms about bonds. None of them can be converted into something that is superimposable on methylpropane.

To complete your work on this section look at the structures in Figure 1.11.

$$CH_3 - CH - CH_2 - CH_2 - CH_3 \qquad\qquad CH_3 - CH_2 - CH - CH_2 - CH_3$$
$$\qquad\quad | \qquad\qquad\qquad\qquad\qquad\qquad\qquad\qquad\qquad\qquad\qquad |$$
$$\qquad\quad CH_3 \qquad\qquad\qquad\qquad\qquad\qquad\qquad\qquad\qquad\quad CH_3$$

**A**                                         **B**

$$CH_3 - CH - CH_3 \qquad\qquad\qquad CH_3 - CH_2$$
$$\qquad\quad | \qquad\qquad\qquad\qquad\qquad\qquad\qquad |$$
$$\qquad\quad CH_2 - CH_2 - CH_3 \qquad\qquad CH_2 - CH_2 - CH_2 - CH_3$$

**C**                                         **D**

$$CH_3 - CH_2 - CH_2 - CH - CH_3 \qquad\qquad CH_3 - CH - CH_2 - CH_3$$
$$\qquad\qquad\qquad\qquad\quad | \qquad\qquad\qquad\qquad\qquad\qquad\qquad\quad |$$
$$\qquad\qquad\qquad\qquad\quad CH_3 \qquad\qquad\qquad\qquad\qquad\qquad CH_2 - CH_3$$

**E**                                         **F**

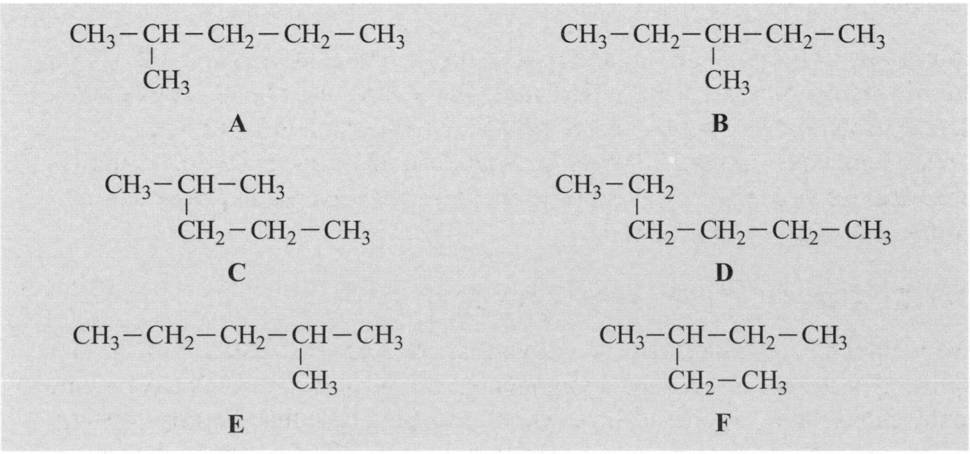

**Figure 1.11**   Structural formulae for $C_6H_{14}$.

### Question 1.1

How many *different* compounds are represented by the structures in Figure 1.11? ◀

# 1.7 Small but important – a model of the atom

In Section 1.4 you looked at some of the outcomes of atoms of elements combining together to give molecules of compounds. In order to understand why different compounds have different properties (and therefore uses) some understanding of *how* and *why* atoms are able to form bonds is required. What are these bonds and why do they form? They are certainly nothing like the grey plastic sticks of your model kit!

To deal with these questions some understanding of the composition of atoms is needed.

## 1.7.1 Atoms

The term atom is now firmly lodged in our vocabulary and has been part of most school curricula for decades. Everyone has heard of atom bombs and atomic (nuclear) energy, even if they are not quite sure what these terms mean, but the existence of atoms is not obvious. It took more than 2000 years for the idea to become accepted. In fact there was still strong opposition to the idea even at the start of the 20th century – probably during our great grandparents' or even grandparents' lifetime!

By the 18th century there was reasonably widespread support for a model of the structure of matter involving some kind of particles. The ideas about earth, air, fire and water being the fundamental substances, the elements, were largely discredited. There was still a great deal of confusion in chemistry and there were numerous unexplained observations. Through experimentation, much was known about chemical change or the changing of one substance into another. By thinking about the experiments and classifying reactions in a number of ways it seemed that elements probably existed, but not of the type the Greeks wrote about. One of the first substances thought to be an element was the alchemists' favourite – gold. The definition developed that an element was something built up from particles unique to that element that could not be created or further subdivided by chemical change. This is still a reasonable working definition of an element.

John Dalton (1766–1844) laid the foundations of modern chemistry with his atomic theory. Starting around 1800 he used the large amount of experimental data, on the relative proportions by mass in which elements combined, accumulated over about 150 years from investigations carried out by other chemical researchers. Almost all of chemistry is now based on properties of atoms and combinations of atoms.

## 1.7.2 The structure of the atom

We now know that atoms are not indivisible. Nuclear energy derives from the splitting of atoms into smaller components, and nuclear physicists have identified many sub-atomic particles. Of those there are only three that directly concern chemists. They are protons, neutrons and electrons. The fact that atoms are not indivisible means that we need to refine our model of the atom. Remember we choose our model to facilitate what we want to think about. Indivisible atoms are fine for many purposes, but no good if we want to think about how bonds are formed. One of the great scientists of the 20th century, Ernest Rutherford (1871–1937), with his assistants Geiger (of Geiger counter fame) and Marsden, devised some clever experiments to investigate the structure of atoms. From the results he obtained, Rutherford put forward a model for the structure of the atom (Figure 1.12). He proposed that the atom is constructed of a very dense core, the nucleus, containing the protons and neutrons, packed very close together. Each proton carries one unit of positive charge, so they repel each other because like charges repel. However, when they are as close together as they are in a nucleus, a very short range force – which is powerful enough to overcome the repulsion – acts to hold the protons together in the nucleus.

Compared with the overall size of the atom the nucleus is very tiny. Rutherford was able to calculate that it is about 1/10 000th of the diameter of an atom, or of the order of $10^{-14}$ m. (If the latter style of writing numbers is not familiar, you will find it useful to have a look at the *Maths Skills Booklet*.) In Rutherford's model of the atom he suggested that the electrons, each carrying one unit of negative charge, orbit the nucleus, rather like a miniature planetary system although, as you will see shortly, this model has now been modified. Although the electrons repel one another, this is overcome by the attraction between the electrons and the positive charges on the protons in the nucleus, because unlike charges attract. An atom of an element is electrically neutral (uncharged) because the number of protons in the nucleus equals the number of electrons in the atom.

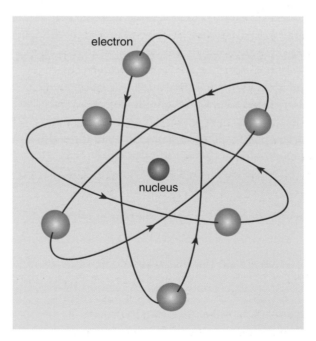

**Figure 1.12**    The Rutherford model of the atom.

Atoms also carry a certain amount of 'ballast' in the nucleus in the form of the third type of particle, the neutron, which bears no charge but does have mass which is almost the same as that of a proton. One element is distinguished from another only by the number of protons each atom contains (which equals the number of electrons, since atoms are electrically neutral). The number of protons in the atom is called its atomic number and the number of protons plus the number of neutrons in one atom is called its mass number. We now have a more quantitative way of saying exactly what an element is – it is a substance the atoms of which all have the same atomic number. There are over 100 elements known, of which 90 are found in nature, and all matter is built from these. Far fewer elements are involved in biological molecules, but there is an almost infinite variety of such molecules, albeit closely related in many cases. Their interactions with each other form the basis of life and the effect of drugs on them underpins the action of modern medicines.

It is possible for different atoms of one element to contain different numbers of neutrons. Atoms that differ only in the numbers of neutrons they contain are called isotopes (Box 1.2).

---

### Box 1.2 Isotopes

Most hydrogen atoms contain just one proton and one electron; they have no neutrons. This type of hydrogen atom is given the symbol H. But there are hydrogen atoms that contain one proton, one neutron and one electron. These are still hydrogen atoms, because the elements are defined by the number of protons, not the number of neutrons. The hydrogen isotope with mass number 2 is one of the very few that have been given their own name and symbol. In this case a hydrogen atom with one proton, one electron and one neutron is called a deuterium atom, symbol D (from the Greek word *deuteros* meaning second). Water containing deuterium atoms instead of hydrogen atoms is often called 'heavy water'.

You may have come across the term isotope in a number of contexts. For example, isotopes are used in medical studies as tracers to investigate the biological processes going on in the body, in the testing of new drugs before they are made available to the general public and for archaeological dating which uses an isotope of carbon (carbon-14 or $^{14}C$), having six protons and eight neutrons. However, chemistry is dominated by protons and electrons and the isotopes of a given element have the same chemical properties, so we shall not be concerned much with them. The term isotope does not necessarily imply radioactivity. Some isotopes are radioactive, some are not. It is radioactive isotopes that are used to provide the radiation needed in radiotherapy treatments.

---

The hydrogen atom is composed of one proton and one electron. It was discovered around 1900 that although the charges of a proton and an electron are equal and opposite, their masses are very different. The proton has a much greater mass than the electron. Over 99.9% of the mass of a hydrogen atom comes from the proton. The electron has only about 1/2000th (more precisely, 1/1836) of the mass of a proton. Since a neutron has almost exactly the same mass as a proton it follows, to a good first approximation, that almost all of the mass of an atom is in the nucleus.

Although Rutherford's model of the structure of the atom formed the basis of modern atomic theory, it soon became necessary to refine it. It turns out that electrons cannot be adequately described as particles similar to billiard balls or marbles. They are usually described as having a dual nature. In some circumstances they behave like charged particles, but at other times they behave like a wave. In describing the behaviour of electrons in atoms, we normally talk about the electron(s) as forming a cloud around the nucleus (Figure 1.13). One way of thinking of the cloud is as the physical expression of the electron acting as a wave; an alternative interpretation is that the cloud shows the probability of finding one or more electrons at a given point, with the electron(s) spending most time where the cloud has the highest density as shown by darker shading.

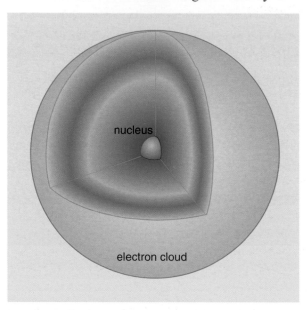

**Figure 1.13**   The modern model of the atom.

We shall not dwell further on the wave nature of electrons as it is not easy to model without using some quite complicated mathematics. The particle model will be fine for our discussions. Do not worry too much about this apparent contradiction; it is something that chemists learn to live with.

The properties of protons, neutrons and electrons are summarised in Table 1.2 for easy reference.

**Table 1.2**   The masses and charges for a proton, a neutron and an electron.

| Particle | Relative mass | Relative charge |
| --- | --- | --- |
| proton | 1 | +1 |
| neutron | 1 | 0 |
| electron | 1/1836 | −1 |

## 1.8   What holds atoms together in molecules – chemical bonding

Now, at last we can start to explain how atoms bond together and form molecules. It turns out that the plastic sticks in the model kit each represent a pair of electrons, one from each of the bonded atoms. The electrons are shared between the atoms and, being negatively charged, are attracted to the positive nuclei of both atoms. Although each atom does not lose its electron completely, it does have to loosen its hold on it to some extent when forming a bond. One would expect, and it turns out to be so, that the shared electrons are the ones that are already furthest from the nucleus of each atom. It does not matter whether our models use the particle model for the electrons in atoms, or the electron cloud model. Either way, the bond comprises two electrons, one from each atom, attracted to the nuclei of both atoms and so holding the atoms together in the molecule. It is called a covalent bond.

### 1.8.1 The shapes of molecules

Now return to the molecular model of methane that you made in Activity 1.1 and we can explain a property of the molecule that it shares with this model.

If the bonds each comprise a pair of electrons it follows that, because they are negatively charged, the bonds will repel each other, so they will try to get as far away from each other as possible. As they are all joined to the same central carbon they are limited as to where they can go and the best all round distribution of the bonds turns out to be when all the bond angles between adjacent bonds are equal (the angle is close to 109.5°, i.e. the tetrahedral angle mentioned in Section 1.6). This idea is known as the electron pair repulsion theory and is often used to account for the shapes or properties of molecules. If you take your model of methane and try bending it a bit so that two of the bonds have a greater angle between them, they will then be further apart. But this geometry, although favourable for them, is at the expense of them moving nearer to the other two bonds. So, just as the model springs back to having all the bond angles equal, so does a real molecule of methane.

The use of molecular models is central to the study of chemistry. For example, it was only by constructing models that Watson and Crick were successful in deducing the structure of DNA, the foundation of the science of molecular genetics. Increasingly, chemists are making use of computer programs that allow the construction of molecular models as images on a screen. But for many chemists, one of the essential tools of the trade is still a model kit. It is a remarkable thing that molecular models of all the substances in the world can be built using a kit of only one hundred or so different types of atoms. Even more remarkable is that for most of the molecules covered in this course only around five different types of atom are needed.

There are different types of model. Some are designed for seeing how a molecule occupies space (Figure 1.14a); these are called space-filling models. There are also models designed simply to show the geometry of molecules; these are called framework models (Figure 1.14b).

**Figure 1.14** Models of a water molecule made using (a) a space-filling model kit, (b) a framework model kit, (c) the ball-and-stick model kit used in the course.

(a)

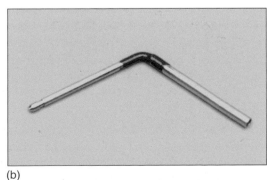

(b)

(c)

The kit you are using in this course shares features both of the space-filling and the framework models. It is called a ball-and-stick model kit and shows the relative geometry of molecules (correct bond angles) while at the same time representing the atoms as spheres (Figure 1.14c).

● Whilst looking at Figure 1.14 you may have spotted something that looks as if it is a contradiction of the electron pair repulsion theory that was used to justify the shape of a methane molecule. If not, look again at Figure 1.14 and see if you can spot what is apparently 'wrong' about it.

● The chemical formula of water is $H_2O$. Checking back to Table 1.1 reveals that oxygen has a valency of two. So, its atom forms two bonds, one to each hydrogen atom. So far, so good, but it then follows that repulsion between these two bonds, causing them to get as far apart as possible, should give us a linear molecule for water, with a bond angle of 180°.

$$H-O-H$$

The 'bent' nature of the water molecule shown in Figure 1.14 arises because of repulsion of the two pairs of bonding electrons by other electrons in the oxygen atom that are not involved in bonding (often referred to as non-bonding electrons). This distorts the molecule from its expected linear shape, giving a bond angle of close to 104.5°. This is an essential part of the molecular structure of water, and helps to determine the structure and properties of liquid water and ice.

 Have a look at an atom of oxygen (red) in the model kit and you will now realise why the holes are drilled where they are. Now look at an atom of nitrogen (blue) from the kit. This has four holes because nitrogen can have a valency of four. When it does, the bonds are tetrahedrally directed, as in methane. But it can also have a valency of three, when only three holes are used. In the latter case it is non-bonding electrons in the nitrogen atom, repelling the bonding electrons, which cause the molecule to assume the shape it does (bond angle 107°) when an atom of nitrogen bonds to three atoms of hydrogen, forming a molecule of ammonia, $NH_3$.

## 1.8.2 The three 'worlds' of chemistry

One of the reasons some people find chemistry puzzling at first is because chemists simultaneously work on three different levels and often switch from one to the other without saying so! The first of these is the macroscopic 'world'; this is the level that deals with descriptive chemistry – the observations that chemists make, for example, methane is a flammable gas. Nowadays, chemists have very powerful instruments that can measure minute amounts of material and provide essential data for a wide variety of purposes. But even if only a nanogram ($10^{-9}$ g or 1 ng) or even a picogram ($10^{-12}$ g or 1 pg) is involved, this is still the macroscopic world (see the *Maths Skills Booklet* for an explanation of *nano-* and *pico-* if these prefixes are new to you).

### Question 1.2

Calculate the number of molecules in 1 nanogram (ng) of the hydrocarbon methane, taking the mass of one molecule of methane to be $3 \times 10^{-23}$ g to one significant figure (see the *Maths Skills Booklet*, for an explanation of the terms *significant figure*, *scientific notation* and *powers of ten*). Your answer should conclude that 1 ng of methane, even though it is a tiny mass, still contains a very large number of molecules so observations of its behaviour are at the macroscopic level. ◀

As discussed, matter is made up of atoms and molecules and chemists interpret observations at the macroscopic level in terms of the behaviour at the molecular level. This then is the second 'world', the molecular level.

The third 'world' is the symbolic level and it connects the other two. This is the level when chemists use formulae, such as $CH_4$ to represent methane. The confusing aspect is that $CH_4$ can sometimes mean a molecule of methane, and it can sometimes mean a few thousand cubic metres of methane in a gas holder! Which of the two is meant at any particular time should be obvious from the context, and in this course it should be clear which level is relevant at any instance. However, you may wish to read other books where the authors have been less explicit about which world they are talking about, so it is just as well to be aware of the three 'worlds' of chemistry.

Another thing chemists are guilty of is to refer to their models as if they are the real thing. If you read carefully through this course you will find that when molecular modelling was first described, the instructions were worded very carefully, e.g. 'use your model kit to make a model of a molecule of methane'. Later in the course you may find this has been shortened to 'use your model kit to make a molecule of methane' or even just 'use your model kit to make methane'. Although perhaps semantically reprehensible, this is what chemists do without in any way meaning to imply that the model *is* methane, just as no-one would make the mistake of believing that any of the models in Figure 1.9 really *is* a human.

When people first started eating herbal remedies, they had no idea of how or why they worked. They just did. At this stage they were not yet working at any of the three levels of chemistry. In the aspirin story people were eventually able to extract the active ingredient from their herb and found it to be a white solid (that they called salicin) with a melting temperature of 201 °C. They had moved into the 'macroscopic world' and were making observations about the properties of their compound.

When chemists started investigating salicin they found it could be converted into another white solid which we now call aspirin. As they could determine the formulae of salicin and aspirin they were then working at the molecular level.

Once chemists were able to construct and draw molecular models of the detailed structures of the two compounds, they had moved on to the symbolic level of understanding. Chapter 2 will pick up this story.

## 1.9   Summary of Chapter 1

In this chapter you have found out that:

- The development of a new medicinal drug from inception to market is a long, expensive process, which relies a great deal on the application of chemical understanding.

- The science of chemistry makes use of a variety of 'models' that represent our understanding but are limited in what they can depict.

- An understanding of chemical bonding within molecules depends on some understanding of the structure of atoms of the elements.

- There are three types of particles within atoms. Protons and neutrons account for most of the mass and are found in the nucleus. Electrons have much smaller mass than protons and neutrons and are found outside the nucleus.

- In molecules the atoms are held together by covalent bonds each comprising a pair of electrons which, as they are negatively charged, are attracted to the positively charged protons in the nuclei of both atoms.

- Because they are negatively charged, each bond repels all the other bonds joined to a given atom, and the non-bonding electrons in that atom, thus dictating the shape of the molecule.

## 1.10 Reflection

Now that you have reached the end of Chapter 1, pause for breath and reflect on what you have achieved. This is a valuable exercise and half an hour spent doing this reflection can pay dividends when you move on to the next chapter of the course.

Try concentrating on three areas.

First, try to think of two or three things that went well whilst working through Chapter 1.

- Write brief notes of what they were and try to think *why* you were happy with them. Perhaps you were familiar with the subject matter, or you studied it at a time of day when you work best. Whatever it was make a note of it!

- Nothing is counted out and these notes are for your eyes only so don't hold back!

Second, try to think of anything that did not go well and, most importantly, *why*. Again, jot down a few notes. Questions you could ask yourself are:

- Did you have to rush through the topics?

- Were you studying when you were tired or frequently disturbed?

- Did you answer the questions, do the activities and make the molecular models as you worked through the chapter or did you try reading straight through it? (There is quite a difference to reading a book and doing an Open University course. The latter is a two-way process in which you interact with the material; just reading something through is often a one-way process, requiring a minimum of interaction.)

- Were you able to talk things through with someone else – possibly someone with whom you live or work? Bouncing ideas off other people is often helpful even if they know little about the topic.

- If anything was puzzling you, did you ask for help? Your course pack contains information on how to get help.

Finally, summarise the changes you made to your study technique whilst working through Chapter 1, or plan to make before Chapter 2.

# Ouch – that hurts!

The relief or avoidance of pain must be one of the major driving forces behind medical research. In this chapter we start the discussion about relief of pain, to be followed by avoidance of pain by local and general anaesthetics in Chapters 4 and 5.

## 2.1 Why does it hurt?

When we experience the sensation of pain it is likely that something is happening that the brain needs to know about, so it can direct us to whatever damage-limiting action is needed. We hurt because we have genes that constructed a body able to feel pain.

Without such a mechanism it is likely that life would be much shorter, with less opportunity to pass on our genetic code. It seems, therefore, that being able to feel pain is a state of affairs favourable to the continuing success of the species. This is unlikely to be foremost in the thoughts of someone who has just broken their leg or poured boiling water over their foot, but the fact remains that feeling pain is part of the defences that enable us to stay alive (Figure 2.1).

## 2.2 How does it hurt?

This is a useful question because once we know the mechanism of pain sensation we can do something about alleviating it.

When tissue is injured there follows a rapid release of 'messenger' chemicals that stimulate the nerve endings. Electrical impulses are relayed through the nerves to the spinal column and to the brain, which registers the sensation of pain. It usually, but not always, also directs our attention to the site where the damaged tissue initiated the pain message.

Drugs to alleviate pain act to interrupt this flow of information. There are three basic types grouped together by the way in which they work.

1   Drugs such as aspirin act at the site of the injury to stop or at least reduce the production of messenger chemicals that stimulate the nerve endings.

2   Another class of drugs, the opiates such as codeine and morphine, act on the central nervous system (brain and spinal cord). Sometimes, the aspirin-like and codeine/morphine-like drugs are combined into one remedy, for example co-codamol and co-proxamol.

3   Local anaesthetics, which will be discussed later in Chapter 4.

For the time being, we will concentrate on aspirin, to illustrate the development of drugs and how they are able to achieve their effects.

## 2.3 The aspirin story

As long ago as 400 BC the physician Hippocrates, from the island of Kos (now a popular Greek holiday destination) prescribed a concoction made from willow leaves to help relieve the pain of childbirth. Ever since then (and probably even before) herbal remedies based on the leaves or bark of willow trees have been

**Figure 2.1**   Pain in action. Feeling pain enables us to stay alive and pass on our genes.

used for the alleviation of pain and fever. In the 1840s the chemists of the day were able to extract the substance salicin from the bark of willow trees by treating it with boiling water. They isolated and identified salicin and found that it was the active ingredient in the pharmacological action of willow bark. This, then, became the lead compound (see Section 1.2) from which other pain-reducing drugs have been developed, including aspirin, of which millions of tablets are taken annually throughout the world.

In 1870 van Nencki, working at the University of Basle, showed that in the body salicin is converted to salicylic acid. As natural products such as salicin usually only occur in small amounts and are often difficult to synthesise, a common strategy is to find a related compound that can easily be made in large amounts in the laboratory (see the 'curare story' in Chapter 5 for an extreme example of this). In this case, salicylic acid looked promising, but treating patients with salicylic acid instead of salicin, whilst affording the same reduction in symptoms, also had the marked disadvantage of causing severe irritation to the mouth, the gullet and the stomach lining – an early example of undesirable side-effects. So this modification of the lead compound salicin was not an improvement. (Salicylic acid can be used to remove warts from the skin, e.g. the preparation sold as 'Compound W®'* – a solution of salicylic acid in acetic acid. Its ability to destroy tissue is then of use!)

A further modification was to convert the salicylic acid into sodium salicylate and see what effect this had. This resulted in a compound that still had the same pharmacological properties as salicylic acid but had the advantage of reduced irritation. A new disadvantage appeared, though – it tasted awful!

The German chemist, Felix Hofmann, then set about modifying the structure of salicylic acid. He made one small change at a time and tested each new product on his father who had rheumatism, until in 1898 he arrived at a product that was as effective as salicylic acid, but lacked the severe irritation and taste problems. This new material was given the name aspirin and, after further clinical trials was manufactured and marketed by the company Bayer, as the first medicinal drug to be available in tablet form.

● Do you think this discussion of aspirin is at the macroscopic, the molecular or the symbolic level? (See Section 1.8.2.)

● The discussion is a combination of macroscopic level with some hints at the molecular level – what the chemists did, what they saw and so on, plus what molecules were involved – but without any representations of the molecules, so no symbolism. In the next section the discussion moves on to the symbolic level.

## 2.4   The molecules involved

### 2.4.1   Salicylic acid

The structural formula of salicylic acid, **2.1**, looks a good bit more complicated than some of the structures you met in Chapter 1. However, it becomes less daunting if you unpack it a bit. One of the first things to do when confronted with

---

* The symbol ® means that the name is a registered trade mark.

an unfamiliar structure is to check that all the valencies are correct (four for carbon, two for oxygen and one for hydrogen). If any atoms have the wrong valency, it follows that there is a mistake somewhere and the molecule does not exist as drawn. It looks OK for the structure of salicylic acid. You probably noticed that some of the carbon atoms have two bonds joining them to another atom. These are called double bonds and they contain four electrons, two per bond. They are quite common in chemical structures. There are two types of double bond in salicylic acid, carbon–carbon double bonds (C=C) and a carbon–oxygen double bond (C=O). Two of the thinner, more flexible bonds in the model kit are used when making models requiring a double bond in the structure. Make a model of each type of double bond in **2.1** and keep them for using later.

Let's have a closer look at the salicylic acid molecule. For a start, focus on the ring part of the structure. If the two groups attached to the ring (the side chains) are removed and replaced with hydrogen atoms, we are left with the hydrocarbon, benzene. This is a liquid, present in coal-tar, which used to be widely used as a solvent by chemists until it was discovered just how poisonous it is. Nowadays benzene is a product of the petrochemical industry.

### Activity 2.1

1   Make a model of a benzene molecule, **2.2**, with your model kit.

●   What do you notice about the model that makes it different to all the previous molecular models that you have made?

●   All the atoms lie in one plane; the ring structure is flat (planar). The presence of the double bonds is the cause of this.

2   Now turn your attention to the rest of the salicylic acid molecule. Remove the hydrogen from one of the benzene's carbons (it does not matter which one) and replace it with an oxygen joined to a hydrogen (an —OH group). When this type of reaction is carried out for real, chemists refer to it as a substitution reaction. The structure that you have made is **2.3**. You may need to rotate *your* model, or the —OH group on it, to match **2.3**.

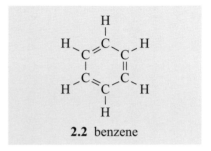

**2.1**  salicylic acid

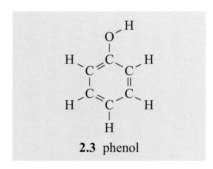

**2.2**  benzene

**2.3**  phenol

Keep this model for later

Note that the C—O—H sequence in **2.3** is not linear, for the same reason given in Section 1.8.1 for the H—O—H sequence in the water molecule. Also the —O—H group in **2.3** can rotate freely around the C—O bond, giving many possible overall shapes for the molecule only one of which is planar.

The presence of the —OH group gives the molecule 2.3 particular properties that are not possessed by benzene. Such a group is called a functional group. The —OH functional group is called a hydroxyl group. If it is joined to any of the hydrocarbon chains shown in Chapter 1 it is an alcohol group, but is more correctly called a phenol (pronounced 'fee-nol') group if it is joined to a benzene ring. The same word, phenol, is also used as the name of the compound you made (**2.3**) consisting of a benzene ring carrying an —OH group and no other substituent groups. You will meet phenol again when you look at bactericides and antiseptics in Chapter 8.

### Activity 2.2

Now look at the other group on the benzene ring in salicylic acid, **2.1**. Make a model of this group and substitute it for another hydrogen atom on your model of phenol. This time you will have to be a bit more particular about which hydrogen atom you substitute. It must be on a carbon atom that is adjacent to the phenol group. There is still some choice, though, as there are two of them.

● Does it matter which of the two carbon atoms you change?

● It appears that perhaps it does, as it looks as if there are two possible isomers. These are **2.4** and **2.5**, and would certainly represent different molecules as they are not superimposable on each other. The difference is that **2.4** has a single bond between the substituted carbons and **2.5** has a double bond between these two carbon atoms. Notice how the structural formulae have been simplified. The benzene ring part of the molecule can just be shown as a hexagon with alternate double and single bonds. Chemists recognise that there is a carbon atom at each of the corners and each carbon atom must carry another group or atom to keep its valency correct. When no group is shown on a corner carbon atom, it is understood that a hydrogen atom is bonded to it. This style stops the drawn structures from getting too cluttered.

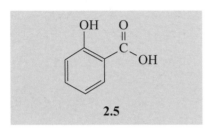

**2.4**

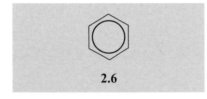

**2.5**

**2.6**

**2.7** salicylic acid

However, it is found that only one product results when the hydrogen atoms on two adjacent carbon atoms in a benzene ring are substituted by any two functional groups. All attempts to make two isomers end up producing the same product. This is an example of failure of the model to depict what the structures really are. In fact neither of structures **2.4** and **2.5** accurately depicts the structure of salicylic acid. A better model is a combination of both of them; you could regard it as a sort of average of the two structures, with one of the bonds in each double bond spread around the ring. This is often shown by drawing a circle in the ring, instead of three double bonds. The circle represents six electrons (two from each of the double bonds) shared round the ring. Structure **2.6** shows the structure of benzene drawn in this style and **2.7** depicts salicylic acid drawn in the same style.

Because the ball-and-stick models are unable to show these 'spread-around-the-ring' electrons, the structures for benzene rings where the double bonds are shown separately will be used. However, where necessary it should be remembered that these double bonds* are shared round the ring. With this in mind, **2.4** and **2.5** turn out to be representations of the same molecule, within the limitations of what the ball-and-stick models can show.

If you were asked to suggest a name for the —OH group on the —COOH group that you have put on the benzene ring, what you have read so far would probably lead you to name it as an alcohol group. However, the close proximity of the C=O part of the molecule changes the properties of the —OH group and makes it

---

* These 'spread-around-the-ring' or 'delocalised' electrons do confer some special properties to benzene and similar compounds. Benzene is said to be 'aromatic' or to have 'aromatic properties'. Although the word aromatic originated because many of these compounds had a characteristic odour it no longer means anything to do with smell – in fact some aromatic compounds have awful smells. It now just means a ring structure with delocalised electrons.

different to the alcohol group. In fact the whole of the group (one carbon, two oxygens and a hydrogen atom) is named as one functional group. It is a carboxylic acid group and has a whole set of chemical properties that make it different to the alcohol group. To simplify writing this functional group it is often abbreviated to $-COOH$ or $-CO_2H$. Some people refer to it as a 'coo' (rhymes with 'blue') group in conversation.

### 2.4.2 The functional group approach

It is the classification of functional groups that simplifies the study of organic chemistry (the chemistry of compounds that contain carbon). With many millions of known organic compounds, and more being added by the day, it would be hopeless if their properties could not be systematised in some way. It turns out that a given functional group usually has the same chemical properties whatever carbon chain it is bonded to, so once the general properties of each functional group are known, all that is left to deal with are the exceptions. It is nearly always the functional groups that undergo change when an organic chemical takes part in a reaction. Fortunately there are relatively few functional groups, some of which are shown in Table 2.1. For convenience, and to keep the valencies correct, these are shown with a hydrocarbon chain attached. It is the shaded bit of each molecule that is the functional group.

Note that functional groups are parts of molecules but they do not exist in isolation. Molecules of compounds like $CH_3CH_2OH$ (Table 2.1) contain the alcohol functional group, $-OH$, but they also include a hydrocarbon chain, $CH_3-CH_2-$. The compound is in the family of compounds called alcohols, all of which have an $-OH$ group attached to a hydrocarbon chain that is often depicted simply by the symbol R.

### 2.4.3 Aspirin

● Compare the structure of aspirin, **2.8**, with that of salicylic acid, **2.7**. What similarities and differences can you see?

● The structures look quite similar. They both have a benzene ring carrying two groups, on adjacent carbon atoms. In both of them one of the groups is a carboxylic acid group. But, salicylic acid carries a phenol group whilst aspirin does not.

● Can you identify the group that is carried by aspirin in the corresponding place to the phenol group in the molecule of salicylic acid? Have a look at options in Table 2.1.

● You should have concluded that this is an ester group. If you did not identify this group correctly, try making a model. Remember there is free rotation about the single bonds and this should enable you to make it look like the ester group in Table 2.1.

You are going to study an important reaction between functional groups on molecules in this section. If you are new to chemistry you may not have seen chemical equations before, so before moving on work through Box 2.1 which provides you with a brief introduction to this topic.

**Table 2.1** The structures of the main functional groups.

| Structure | Name |
| --- | --- |
| $CH_3-CH_2-\boxed{OH}$ | alcohol |
| $CH_3-CH_2-\boxed{NH_2}$ | amine |
| $CH_3-\boxed{CH=CH}-CH_3$ | alkene |
| $CH_3-\overset{\overset{O}{\|\|}}{C}-\underset{OH}{}$ | carboxylic acid |
| $CH_3-\overset{\overset{O}{\|\|}}{C}-O-CH_2-CH_3$ | ester |
| $CH_3-\overset{\overset{O}{\|\|}}{C}-NH_2$ | amide |

**2.8** aspirin

## Box 2.1 An introduction to chemical equations

When chemists want to refer to a chemical reaction in which bonds are broken and new bonds are formed to produce new molecules (the products) from other molecules (the reactants), they often do so by means of a chemical equation. The reactants are shown on the left and the products are on the right.

reactants = products

As atoms cannot be created or destroyed in chemical reactions, the total number of atoms of each element involved must be the same on each side of the equation, if the equation is to 'balance' correctly. The two sides are then linked by an equals (=) sign and the equation is referred to as a 'balanced equation'.

For example, methane – the first molecule you made a model of and a fossil fuel gas – burns in the oxygen of the air to form carbon dioxide ($CO_2$) and water ($H_2O$). The reaction can be represented by the equation:

$$CH_4 + 2O_2 = CO_2 + 2H_2O$$

Count the atoms of each element on the left of the reaction and compare with the numbers on the right. They should be the same! Remember $2O_2$ means $2 \times 2 = 4$ atoms of oxygen (O).

Note the need for two molecules of oxygen and two molecules of water to balance the equation. The information that this equation contains is that one molecule of methane reacts with two molecules of oxygen to produce one molecule of carbon dioxide and two molecules of water.

Sometimes the numbers of the molecules are unimportant and we just want to focus on the formulae of the reactants and products, not how much of each is involved. Chemists often show this type of relationship with a reaction having an arrow ($\rightarrow$) instead of an equals sign. The following reaction is in this style:

$$CH_4 + O_2 \rightarrow CO_2 + H_2O$$

## 2.5 Some chemistry involving esters

Esters are produced by the reaction of a carboxylic acid with an alcohol and result from the formation of a new bond (Reaction 2.1). For example, ethyl butanoate, the major constituent of artificial pineapple flavouring, is made from the reaction of butanoic acid with ethanol.

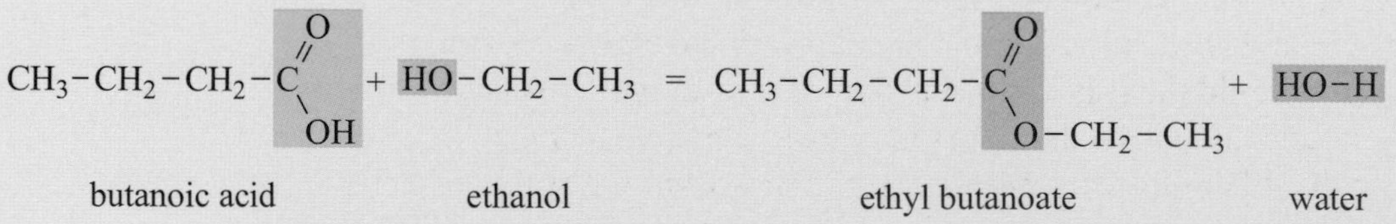

$$CH_3-CH_2-CH_2-\overset{\displaystyle O}{\underset{\displaystyle OH}{C}} \; + \; HO-CH_2-CH_3 \; = \; CH_3-CH_2-CH_2-\overset{\displaystyle O}{\underset{\displaystyle O-CH_2-CH_3}{C}} \; + \; HO-H \qquad (2.1)$$

butanoic acid          ethanol                    ethyl butanoate                water

There is a certain logic to the naming of these compounds. Note the endings on the names: -ic for the carboxylic acid, -ol for the alcohol and -ate for the ester. A complete explanation of the formal rules for naming chemical compounds is well beyond what you need in SK185 but see Box 3.1 for some of the complications involved.

Because the other product is water, this type of reaction is known as a condensation reaction*. This reaction is common to nearly all carboxylic acids, $R^1COOH$, and alcohols, $R^2OH$. So, we can write the general reaction, 2.2, where the abbreviation $R^1$ represents the rest of the carboxylic acid molecule and $R^2$ represents the rest of the alcohol molecule. Check through Reactions 2.1 and 2.2 and make sure you can follow the way in which some of the atoms move from one molecule to another as the reaction takes place. We have colour coded the reacting groups in Reactions 2.1 and 2.2 to help you see this change.

$$
R^1-\underset{OH}{\overset{O}{C}} \;+\; HO-R^2 \;=\; R^1-\underset{O-R^2}{\overset{O}{C}} \;+\; HO-H \qquad (2.2)
$$

carboxylic acid        alcohol                    ester            water

You will meet another condensation reaction in Section 3.1 on protein formation.

The use of the symbol R to represent the rest of the molecule is common in organic chemistry. It enables us to focus on the parts of the molecules that matter (the functional groups) without the formulae being cluttered up with the parts that are not reacting.

● What are the structures of the carboxylic acid and alcohol that you would use to make isopentyl acetate, **2.9**, a constituent of banana oil? (*Hint*: you need to identify $R^1$ and $R^2$.)

● Reaction 2.3 shows the required structures (and their names, which you have not met before).

$$
CH_3-\overset{O}{C}\underset{O-CH_2-CH_2-CH}{} \; \underset{CH_3}{\overset{CH_3}{}}
$$

**2.9**

$$
CH_3-\underset{OH}{\overset{O}{C}} \;+\; HO-CH_2-CH_2-\underset{CH_3}{\overset{CH_3}{CH}} \;=\; CH_3-\overset{O}{C}\underset{O-CH_2-CH_2-\underset{CH_3}{\overset{CH_3}{CH}}}{} \;+\; H_2O \qquad (2.3)
$$

acetic acid              isopentanol                      isopentyl acetate            water

An important thing about this reaction is that, although it shows an ester *forming* from a carboxylic acid and an alcohol, it could equally well have been written the other way round. It would then show the reaction of an ester with water, to produce a carboxylic acid and an alcohol. This is an example of a chemical reaction that can run in either direction, rather unsurprisingly known as a reversible reaction. They are very common and sometimes you see the use of the symbol ⇌, instead of =. The reverse of the condensation reaction above is known as a hydrolysis reaction, reflecting the fact that it is reaction with water. The word is derived from *hydro* (water) and *lysis* (splitting), so hydrolysis is literally *splitting with water*, which accounts for the fact that any hydrolysis reaction gives two products.

* There are other condensation reactions that do not involve the formation of water, but they do involve two molecules joining together to form a larger molecule with the elimination of a different smaller molecule, e.g. ammonia or hydrogen chloride, instead of water. We will not be concerned with these other condensation reactions.

### Question 2.1

Identify the ester groups in the compounds shown in Figure 2.2. Write down the reactions that produce each of the esters and thus deduce the structures of the carboxylic acids and alcohols needed to make them. ◀

**Figure 2.2** Some esters. For use with Question 2.1.

Now look back to the structures of salicylic acid, **2.7**, and aspirin, **2.8**.

● See if you can pick out the carboxylic acid that is involved in converting the phenol group in salicylic acid into the ester group in aspirin.

● You should have decided it was $CH_3$—COOH, acetic acid, but may well have written its formula in a different style or shape. This does not matter, it is still acetic acid so long as the atoms are joined together in the same order as in our structure,

### Activity 2.3

Complete your study of the relationship between salicylic acid, acetic acid and aspirin by making models of salicylic acid, **2.7**, and acetic acid. Place them side by side so that the phenol group (—OH) of the salicylic acid is next to the —COOH of the acetic acid. Then remove the H atom from the phenol and the —OH from the acetic acid and join the two fragments together. You have made an aspirin molecule, **2.8**. What else have you made?

The other compound that you have made is water, $H_2O$ (remember this is a condensation reaction), provided you joined the unwanted H atom to the —OH. The complete reaction is shown in Figure 2.3.

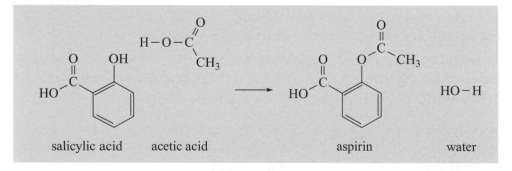

**Figure 2.3** Reaction between salicylic acid and acetic acid to form aspirin.

You should be able to see how the reaction in Figure 2.3 can take place in the reverse direction (hydrolysis), with the water molecule splitting the aspirin molecule into molecules of salicylic acid and acetic acid. If you have an old bottle of aspirin tablets you may find they have a slight smell of vinegar, especially if they have become damp. As you have seen, when aspirin reacts with water the carboxylic acid that it forms, by hydrolysis of the ester group, is acetic acid. This is the compound responsible for the smell of vinegar.

## 2.6   How does aspirin relieve pain?

Aspirin acts at the site of damaged tissue to block the start of the nerve signal to the brain, the mechanism by which we experience pain (Section 2.2). It does this by inhibiting the formation of prostaglandin which is the active agent responsible for the sensitisation of the nerve endings. Prostaglandins (there are several related types) are responsible for a lot of physiological events in addition to the start of the pain signal at the nerve ending. For example, they are responsible for inflammation, fever and the clotting of platelets in the blood, so it is easy to see why aspirin is such a useful drug. However, a prostaglandin also increases the formation of protective mucus in the gut, so aspirin-induced suppression of its formation can cause irritation and bleeding.

Before an explanation of aspirin's activity at the molecular level can be developed some more chemical ideas are needed. Prostaglandins are synthesised in the body's cells from arachidonic acid, **2.10**. This is a carboxylic acid containing a chain of 20 carbon atoms in its molecule. **2.10** shows this structure using the style developed in Chapter 1.

$$CH_3CH_2CH_2CH_2CH_2CH=CHCH_2CH=CHCH_2CH=CHCH_2CH=CHCH_2CH_2CH_2-COOH$$

**2.10**  arachidonic acid

Although this structure looks rather complicated at first, it is relatively simple in that it has an unbranched carbon chain terminating in a carboxylic acid group. It does have the added complication of four carbon–carbon double bonds but the real influence of these is not apparent until one looks at the shape of the molecule. We have made a model of **2.10** and photographed it, but before we look at that you need to return to your model kit and have a look at the shape surrounding the atoms joined by a carbon–carbon double bond.

### Activity 2.4

1   Make a model of the compound ethene, $C_2H_4$, using the appropriate number of bonds and keeping the valencies correct for all the atoms.

You should have found that you needed a double bond between the two carbon atoms (remember to use two of the longer bonds in the kit for this) and should have ended up with the structure shown in Figure 2.4.

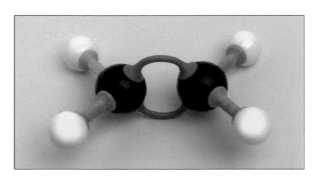

**Figure 2.4**   A model of ethene.

If you think back to previous models you made, you should recall ethane, $CH_3—CH_3$, the second member of the homologous series known as the alkanes. Note the similarity in the names. The ending –ane has been changed to –ene, but the rest of the name (eth-) is preserved because it refers to the fact that there are two carbon atoms in the molecule. Ethene is the simplest member of the homologous series known as the alkenes. The simplest alkane, methane, does not have a counterpart in the alkene series, as it is not possible to have a double bond if there is only one carbon atom in the molecule. After this, though, the alkenes follow a similar naming sequence as the alkanes, so you have propene, butene and so on.

2    Now take your model of ethene. Remove one of the hydrogen atoms, extend the carbon chain by one carbon atom and add the appropriate number of hydrogen atoms to keep all the valencies correct. You now have a model of a propene molecule.

This should have been straightforward enough and our model is depicted in Figure 2.5.

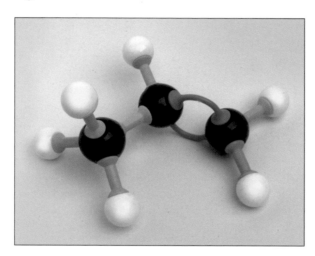

**Figure 2.5**    A model of propene.

3    Now take your model of propene and extend it by one carbon atom plus the appropriate number of hydrogen atoms to make a molecule of $C_4H_8$.

You probably found this less straightforward as you could join the extra carbon atom to any one of the three carbon atoms in propene and it looks as if you end up with several different molecules. (Remember the principle of superimposability, Section 1.6, to test whether things are the same or not.)

The molecules are shown in Figure 2.6. All these molecules exist and we need a way of naming them that makes it clear which molecule is being discussed.

The structure shown in Figure 2.6d does not present a problem. If you look back to how the branched chain version of butane was named in Section 1.4, you will see that it was called methylpropane. By the same strategy Figure 2.6d is named methylpropene.

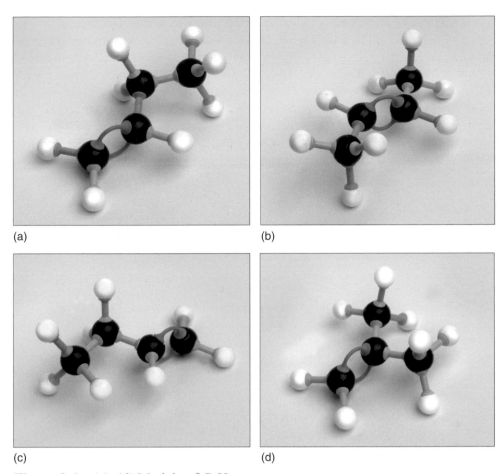

**Figure 2.6** (a)–(d) Models of $C_4H_8$.

$$CH_2=CH-CH_2-CH_3 \qquad CH_3-CH=CH-CH_3 \qquad CH_3-CH_2-CH=CH_2$$
$$\;\;1\quad\;\; 2\quad\;\; 3\quad\;\; 4 \qquad\qquad\;\; 1\quad\;\; 2\quad\;\; 3\quad\;\; 4 \qquad\qquad\;\; 1\quad\;\; 2\quad\;\; 3\quad\;\; 4$$

(a)          (b)          (c)

**Figure 2.7** Numbering the carbon chain in molecules of $C_4H_8$.

Before attempting to name the remaining structures, Figure 2.6a–c, we need a way to identify exactly which carbon atoms are joined to the double bond. This is done by numbering the chain, starting at one end, as shown in Figure 2.7.

As Figure 2.6a and b cannot be exactly superimposed on each other they are molecules of different compounds. They are named but-1-ene and but-2-ene, respectively, the number in the name designating the lowest numbered carbon atom in the chain to which the double bond is joined. It might be expected that Figure 2.6c is but-3-ene but this is not the case because it is identical to but-1-ene (Figure 2.6a). It can be picked up, turned over and superimposed on but-1-ene, so is the same – try it with your models. By convention the lowest possible number(s) is always used in a name whenever there is more than one option. Because but-1-ene, but-2-ene and methylpropene have the same molecular formula ($C_4H_8$) but different structural formulae (showing which atoms are joined to which) they are isomers (Section 1.4).

You might have found that but-2-ene created a problem in that you needed to decide which side of the double bond to place the two —CH₃ groups and the two hydrogen atoms. Our models are shown in Figure 2.8.

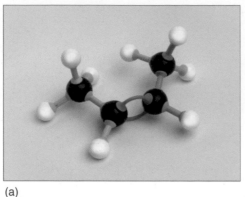 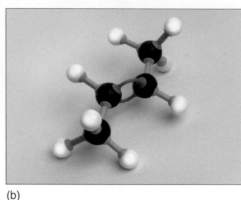

(a)                              (b)

**Figure 2.8**   Models of (a) *cis*-but-2-ene and (b) *trans*-but-2-ene.

The problem was caused by an important feature of the model that is also possessed by the molecule itself. Two carbon atoms joined by a double bond cannot rotate relative to each other. This part of the molecule is therefore much more rigid than parts built with just single bonds. *Cis*-but-2-ene and *trans*-but-2-ene have the same structural formula and the same sequence of atoms is present in both. However, their *geometry* differs so one cannot be superimposed on the other, so they really are different compounds. They are known as geometrical isomers, or *cis/trans* isomers (Latin: *cis*, on this side; *trans*, across).

Returning to the structural formula of arachidonic acid, introduced earlier, the implications soon become apparent. The double bonds control the shape of the molecule.

$$CH_3CH_2CH_2CH_2CH_2CH=CHCH_2CH=CHCH_2CH=CHCH_2CH=CHCH_2CH_2CH_2-COOH$$

**2.10**  arachidonic acid

There are four double bonds in the molecule, each of which can be *cis* or *trans*, so generating a pair of geometrical isomers. If all the different geometrical isomers of **2.10** are modelled that makes a total of 16 different possibilities in all! However, because double bonds prevent rotation within the molecule only *one* of the 16 isomers has the atoms in the correct place to form prostaglandin. The relevant isomer is the one where all the double bonds are *cis*, as shown in Figure 2.9. This isomer needs to react with oxygen and form the ring near the middle of the carbon chain (Figure 2.10). If any of the double bonds are *trans*, the atoms are too far apart to react to form the five-membered ring and the structure shown in Figure 2.10 could not form.

The formation of a five-membered ring in the arachidonic acid molecule to produce prostaglandin could not take place in the body without the action of enzyme molecules. These are compounds that increase the rates of reactions in living systems.

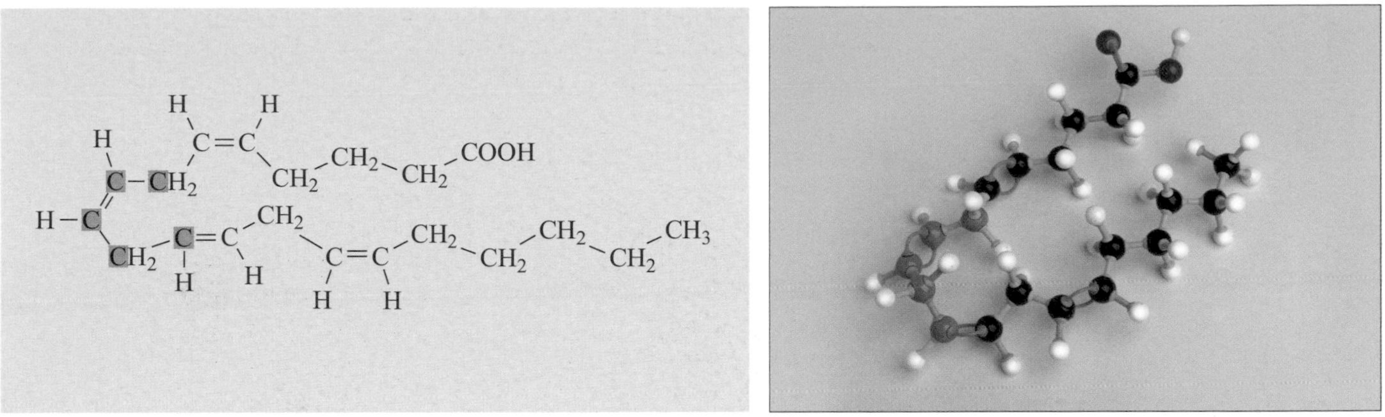

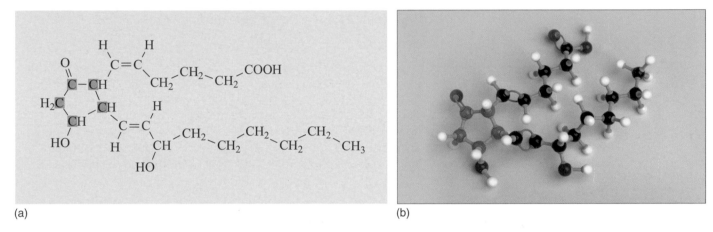

(a)  (b)

**Figure 2.9** (a) Structure and (b) model of an arachidonic acid molecule. *Note*: the five carbon atoms in arachidonic acid highlighted in purple are the ones that end up in the five-membered ring in prostaglandin (Figure 2.10). The same five carbon atoms are purple in the model.

(a)  (b)

**Figure 2.10** (a) Structure and (b) model of a prostaglandin molecule, formed by reaction of arachidonic acid with oxygen and cyclisation (ring formation).

## 2.7 Enzymes

It will probably come as no surprise to you that chemical reactions, including the conversion of arachidonic acid into prostaglandin, do not occur instantaneously and the rate at which they take place can be very variable. Some reactions are over in a flash, such as the burning of gunpowder, and others take months, such as rust formation on a car. All chemical reactions can be speeded up by increasing the temperature of the reactants. In the laboratory one often 'cooks' reaction mixtures for, say, 30 minutes at 100 °C to make them react at a useful speed. However, the human body does not have this facility and has found alternative ways of speeding up the many chemical reactions that it needs to carry out.

Nearly all of the chemical transformations that go on in the body are helped along by enzymes. Enzymes are nature's catalysts, enabling otherwise slow reactions to occur rapidly. Enzymes are very effective at their job, enabling large numbers of reactions that would otherwise require quite extreme conditions, to be carried out in the body. Like all catalysts, enzymes are not used up or changed by the reactions they are speeding up. They are also highly specific in their action so many different enzymes are required to cope with all the different chemical reactions needed to keep our bodies working. For example, enzymes known as lipases assist with the digestion of fats by increasing the rate of hydrolysis of the ester groups within the fat molecules. The enzyme cyclooxygenase (COX) catalyses the formation of prostaglandin from arachidonic acid.

### 2.7.1  How enzymes work

Enzyme molecules have an 'active site' that is a specific shape for a given enzyme. It is here that reactant molecules are converted into products. The active site binds to and holds the reactant molecule in exactly the right position for the reaction to take place. Effectively it fits around the molecule rather like a glove fits around a hand. This very precise three-dimensional structure can only be achieved by enzymes being large complex molecules. Chapter 3 deals with some of the detail of how reactants can bind to enzymes.

Because the enzyme fits the reactant like a glove, the active site will accommodate only a very small range of different molecules. The enzyme is said to be highly specific in its action. The relationship between enzyme and reactant has been likened to a lock and key (Figure 2.11); the enzyme is like a lock where only one type of key, the correct reactant, will fit the active site. Thus only a very specifically shaped molecule will interact with the enzyme and undergo a reaction. In Figure 2.11, although the three possible reactant molecules all have very similar shapes, only one can fit into the active site.

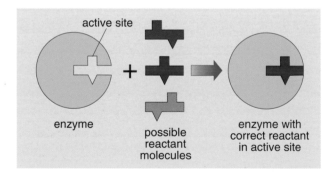

**Figure 2.11**  'Lock and key' representation of the active site in an enzyme.

There are usually several steps in a chemical reaction – the reactants do not just disappear and turn into products without passing through a number of intermediate stages. This sequence of intermediate reactions is called the reaction mechanism. Catalysis occurs by the enzyme being intimately involved in the mechanism. Figure 2.12 shows a schematic representation of the stages that are involved. Enzymes provide an alternative, faster, reaction mechanism. In early stages of the mechanism the enzyme reacts with the reactant to give intermediates; however, the enzyme is regenerated in a later stage. Thus, the catalyst, an enzyme, is not consumed; it is continually recycled so one molecule of enzyme can catalyse the conversion of many reactant molecules into product molecules. Only a small amount of the catalyst is required. Since the catalyst is not consumed, it does not end up as part of the product and the overall reaction product is the same irrespective of whether it is catalysed or not; the catalyst merely speeds up the reaction.

The way that enzymes work is an area of great interest to chemists, because if we know how enzymes control the conversion of reactants into products then it gives the chemist the opportunity to help out when things go wrong. You will see the importance of this approach as we return to it several times in the course.

## 2.7.2 Formation of prostaglandin

Figure 2.13 models the way that the enzyme cyclooxygenase (COX) catalyses the formation of prostaglandin from arachidonic acid. Note how important the shape of the arachidonic acid molecule is. It needs to be just right to match the shape of the active site on the COX molecule and, as you have seen, of the 16 possible geometrical isomers, only one will fit. The one with all the double bonds *cis* has all the atoms in the right place to fit into the cavity containing the active site of COX and is the right shape to cyclise and form prostaglandin.

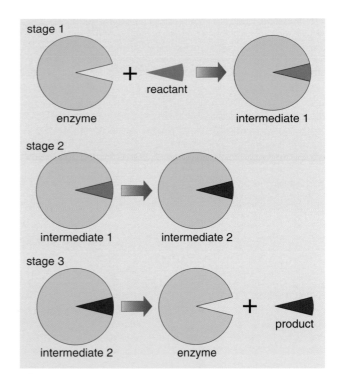

**Figure 2.12** Schematic representation of the three stages of enzyme activity.

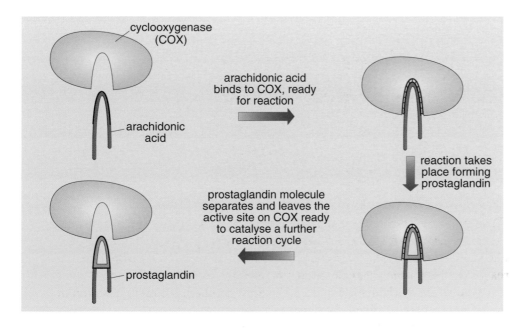

**Figure 2.13** Enzyme-catalysed formation of prostaglandin from arachidonic acid.

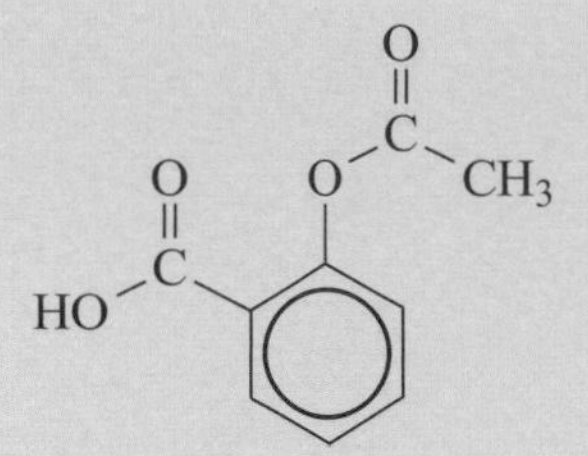

**2.8  aspirin**

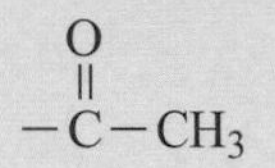

**Figure 2.14** An acetyl group, part of the ester group of aspirin.

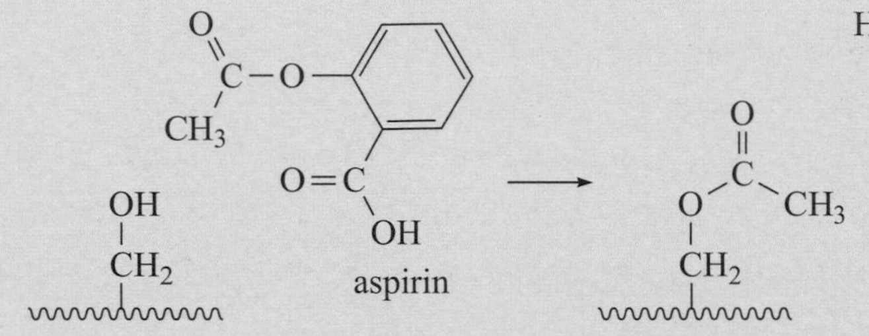

**Figure 2.15** The acetyl group in aspirin reacts with an alcohol group inside the COX cavity.

## 2.8  Enter aspirin!

Aspirin is able to release part of its ester group (Figure 2.14) in a hydrolysis reaction. Look again at the structure of aspirin, **2.8**, and identify this group on the molecule. It is known as an acetyl group and accounts for aspirin also being called acetylsalicylic acid. The acetyl group on aspirin is fairly easily removed and can be available for forming another ester with an alcohol (−OH group) on another molecule; in this case, part of the structure that makes up the inside of the cavity in COX (Figure 2.15). The wiggly line in this reaction represents the rest of the COX molecule.

COX molecule → acetylated COX

The −OH group in the COX cavity has become acetylated, i.e. had an acetyl group added to it. Quite simply this just makes the cavity of the active site of COX smaller. The arachidonic acid is no longer able to enter the cavity, so prostaglandin does not form, so the pain is relieved (Figure 2.16). This acetylation involves the formation of a covalent bond (Section 1.8) which is strong, so the acetyl group is not readily released and aspirin continues to relieve pain for quite a long time after the dose is taken.

**Figure 2.16** Arachidonic acid unable to bind to acetylated COX.

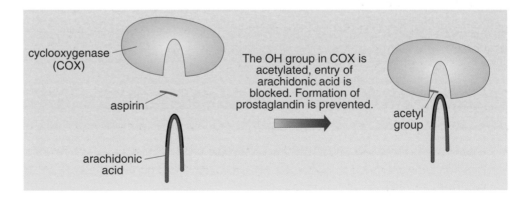

cyclooxygenase (COX)

aspirin

arachidonic acid

The OH group in COX is acetylated, entry of arachidonic acid is blocked. Formation of prostaglandin is prevented.

acetyl group

### Question 2.2

Write a list of the main events in 'the story of aspirin', from the time of Hippocrates to when Bayer started marketing aspirin, and identify the matching steps in Figure 1.3. ◀

### Question 2.3

What is the *molecular* formula of aspirin? ◀

**Question 2.4**

Make a model of a molecule of *cyclohexane*, a hydrocarbon with molecular formula $C_6H_{12}$ that contains a six-membered ring of carbon atoms. Compare it to a model of benzene and comment on their different shapes. ◄

**Question 2.5**

Each cell in the human body accommodates around 2000 different enzymes but only a small quantity of each one. Why are there so many and why is only a small quantity of each required? ◄

## 2.9 Summary of Chapter 2

In this chapter you have found out that:

- The sensation of pain is caused by the release of a chemical (prostaglandin) that stimulates the nerve endings and sends an electrical message to the brain.

- Pain can be reduced if the formation of prostaglandin can be inhibited.

- Prostaglandin is formed, from arachidonic acid, in a cavity in the active site of the enzyme cyclooxygenase (COX).

- Geometrical isomerism can be important in controlling the shape of molecules.

- The specific shape of the arachidonic acid molecule is caused by four carbon–carbon double bonds in its carbon chain which limit the rotation allowed within the molecule. Only one of the isomers, in which all four double bonds are *cis*, has the atoms in the correct place for prostaglandin formation.

- Aspirin can release an acetyl group, which bonds to the active site of COX and prevents arachidonic acid from entering the cavity, so inhibiting the formation of prostaglandin.

## 2.10 Reflection

Now that you have completed another chapter it would be a good time to go through the reflection process that you first did at the end of Chapter 1. You might like to extend it to include the following questions:

- Did the changes to your study technique made during, or at the end of, the last chapter improve your effectiveness?

- Were any other changes needed, perhaps arising from the different subject matter?

- Have you started to become familiar with some of the language of chemistry? It is not something that happens rapidly, so please don't let the language prevent you from moving on through the course.

- By now you should have started to see the importance of making models to help understand the molecular structures in the text.

- Can you recognise some of the functional groups in a molecule? [Remember the course does not *require* you to memorise facts like these as for an exam, but with frequent use you should be starting to remember some of the information.]

- Question 2.1 was not an easy one. If you found it tough, now would be a good time to go back to it and have another look. Being able to find the right answers to this question now would be ample evidence that you have started to become familiar with some important functional groups and reactions.

# 3  Enzymes – nature's facilitators

Chapter 2 described in general terms how enzymes function to speed up reactions in living systems and applied this to how aspirin interferes with the conversion of arachidonic acid into prostaglandin in the active site of the enzyme cyclooxygenase (COX). Enzymes are proteins so, before dealing with how they work, some protein chemistry is required. We will then explain how reactant molecules bind to enzymes, followed by some more detail on the production of prostaglandin and finish the topic with a brief look at some alternatives to aspirin.

## 3.1  Proteins

Most people would associate the term protein with foods, such as soya, eggs, cheese or meat. Some proteins turn up in nature as the structural part of tissue – as in muscle, tendons and hair – whilst others are important parts of cells, as the molecules that carry out and control many of the bodily functions. All proteins are long-chain molecules, known as biopolymers. Polymer molecules are formed by joining together many small molecules, known as monomers, to give long chain-like molecules, sometime called macromolecules (Greek: *makros*, meaning long).

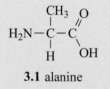

**3.1** alanine

The small molecules that join together to make proteins are amino acids. Alanine, also known as 2-aminopropanoic acid, **3.1**, is a typical example.

Before we move on with our work on proteins we will explain (Box 3.1) a little about the annoying habit that chemists have, of giving everything at least two names.

---

### Box 3.1  What's in a name?

There are few things that do not have at least one alternative name and chemistry is no exception. There are common names (sometimes referred to as 'trivial' names) and so-called 'systematic' names for most compounds. Both styles have their advantages and disadvantages. Unless you know that alanine has the structure shown in **3.1**, you cannot work it out from the name. However, given the systematic name, *2-aminopropanoic acid*, with a bit of experience it is possible to work out what structure this implies. So systematic names have the advantage so far.

However, for large molecules the systematic names become very long. For example, if you look back to Chapter 2 you will see the formula of arachidonic acid, **2.10**. Arachidonic acid is a trivial name. Its systematic name is *5,8,11,14-eicosatetraenoic acid*, so you can see why chemists tend to use trivial names for these large molecules – and arachidonic acid is not really a particularly big molecule compared with others involved in reactions in the human body. Try saying 'Please pass the *α-D-glucopyranosyl-β-D-fructofuranoside*' (Figure 3.1) the next time you want some sugar for your coffee! The trivial names will usually be adopted when referring to compounds in this course.

"One α-D-glucopyranosyl-β-D-fructofuranoside or two?"

**Figure 3.1**   The chemists' tea-break.

- Using the structures of functional groups from Table 2.1 that are also reproduced on the bookmark, identify the functional groups in alanine, **3.1**.

- You should have been able to pick out a carboxylic acid group ($-COOH$) and an amine group ($-NH_2$). Alanine is known as an amino acid.

Note the methyl ($-CH_3$) side-chain in the alanine molecule. In fact there are 20 or so different common naturally occurring amino acids, each of which is characterised by its own side-chain. Some of them are shown in Figure 3.2.

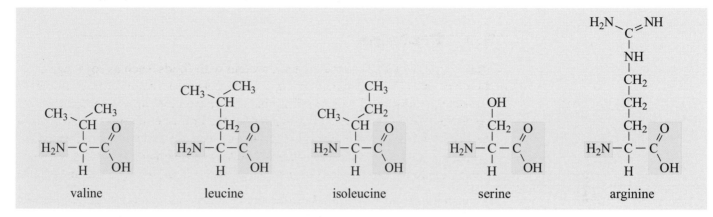

**Figure 3.2**   The amino acids valine, leucine, isoleucine, serine and arginine.

- What are the common structural features of the amino acids in Figure 3.2?

- They all contain an amine group and a carboxylic acid group attached to a carbon atom. These groups are highlighted in Figure 3.2.

Structure **3.2** shows the general structure of all the amino acids involved in the formation of protein molecules. It is the different R groups (R = rest of the molecule) that give each amino acid its unique properties.

So, how do amino acids react together to give proteins? You may remember the condensation reaction in Section 2.5 in which esters are formed by an alcohol reacting with a carboxylic acid. It happens that a hydrogen atom bonded to a nitrogen atom has some very similar properties to a hydrogen atom bonded to an oxygen atom. So, the reaction between a carboxylic acid and an amine (Reaction 3.1) is similar to the reaction between a carboxylic acid and an alcohol (Reaction 2.2). The same colour coding has been used in both reactions.

$$\underset{\text{carboxylic acid}}{R^1-C\overset{O}{\underset{OH}{\big|\big|}}} + \underset{\text{amine}}{\overset{H}{\underset{H}{N-R^2}}} = \underset{\text{amide}}{R^1-C\overset{O}{\underset{\underset{H}{N-R^2}}{\big|\big|}}} + \underset{\text{water}}{H_2O} \qquad (3.1)$$

One of the products, this time, is not an ester but is an amide. Just as alcohols react with carboxylic acids to give esters, so amines react with carboxylic acids to give amides. As you may have expected, a molecule of water is also formed as a consequence of this condensation reaction.

### 3.1.1   Amides

● Draw the product that results when the carboxylic acid group of alanine, **3.1**, reacts with the amine group of valine (Figure 3.2).

● Following the pattern of Reaction 3.1 gives Reaction 3.2, where the functional groups involved in the reaction are highlighted.

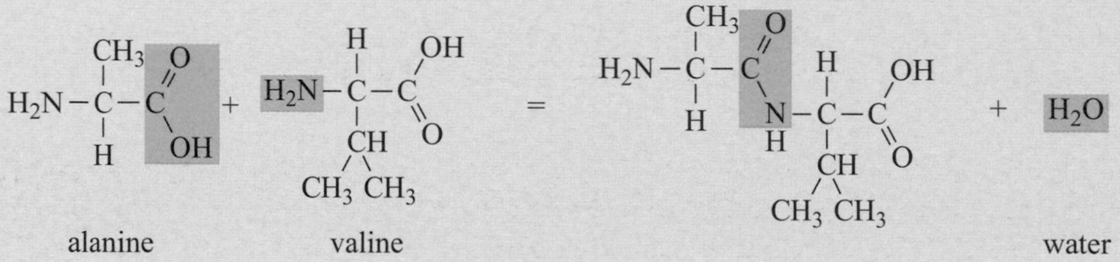

Note that the product of this reaction, with its amide group near the middle of the molecule, still has an amine group at one end and a carboxylic acid group at the other, so it could react with another molecule of an amino acid at either end. This is the basis of the formation of a polymer if the reaction is repeated many times. Figure 3.3 shows just four amino acids forming part of such a chain; a typical protein would have a very much longer chain.

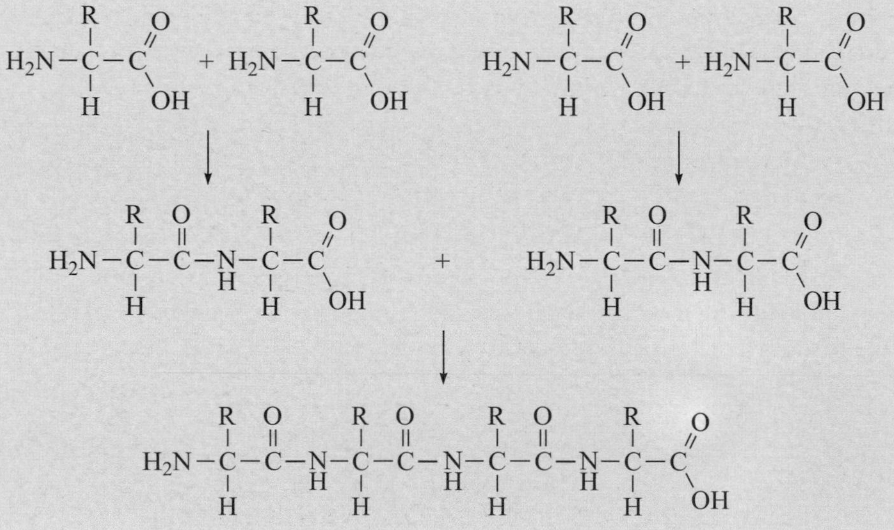

**Figure 3.3**   A generalised representation of the formation of a protein from amino acids. In each step a molecule of water is lost.

The amide group is often referred to as a peptide group, especially when part of a protein chain  A peptide or amide bond is the C—N bond that joins two amino acid residues together in the protein chain. In Figure 3.3 the all-important bond is shown in red. Whether you choose to call it an amide bond or a peptide bond is somewhat arbitrary.

**Question 3.1**

Draw structures to show how four molecules of leucine could react together by the formation of peptide bonds, also forming three molecules of water. ◀

However many amino acids are added to the chain it will always have an amine group at one end and a carboxylic acid group at the other, so very long chains can be built up. The convention used is that the unreacted amine group at the end of the chain is always shown on the left and the carboxylic acid group always on the right (Figure 3.3). These are known as 'terminal groups' because they occur at the end of the chain.

Although the *backbone* of the protein polymer has the same repeating unit (**3.3**), the side-chains (R— groups) vary along the chain for different proteins, generating a wide variety of possibilities. With roughly 20 amino acids to choose from and each chain containing hundreds and sometimes thousands of amino acid units, it is clear that the number of different possible protein molecules is almost limitless. By way of example it can be calculated that, for a medium-sized protein chain (also known as a polypeptide by virtue of its many peptide bonds) containing 288 amino acid units chosen from only 12 different amino acids, there are theoretically over $10^{300}$ different chains possible. That's 1 with 300 zeros written after it! However, as you might imagine, in nature nothing is left to chance, especially with such long odds of forming just one particular sequence in a chain. When proteins are made, the organism's DNA carefully controls the identity and order in which the different amino acids appear in the chain, leading to protein molecules with very specific structures, each with their own properties and uses. The unit that each amino acid contributes to the protein polymer is known as the amino acid residue, as shown in Figure 3.4a. The sequence of amino acid residues in a particular protein is known as the primary structure of the protein. For convenience, when writing out the sequence of amino acid residues, rather than drawing out the structure, a three-letter code is often used to show the order, as shown in Figure 3.4b.

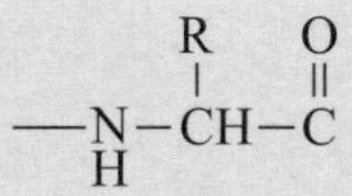

$$\begin{array}{c} R \quad\; O \\ |\quad\;\; \| \\ -N-CH-C \\ | \\ H \end{array}$$

**3.3**

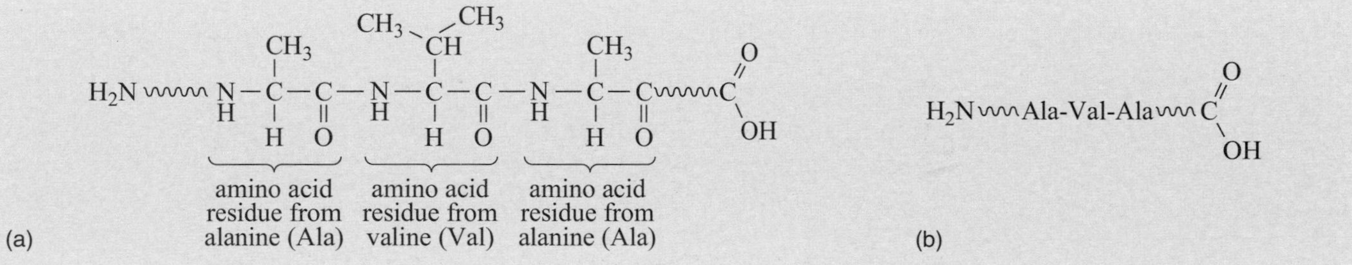

**Figure 3.4**  Representations of part of a protein chain: (a) using structural formulae; (b) using the three-letter code for the amino acid residues. (The wavy lines represent the rest of a long chain of atoms.)

$-NH_2$
amide

$$-\overset{\displaystyle O}{\underset{\displaystyle \|}{C}}-OH$$

carboxylic acid

Figure 3.5 shows the amino acid residue sequence of the primary structure of vasopressin, a hormone that is involved with controlling water balance in the body. Although the vasopressin molecule is not really big enough to be called a protein and ends in an amide rather than a carboxylic acid (see margin), it does have one of the basic molecular features of proteins. This is a precise sequence of amino acids joined together by peptide bonds. The amino acids involved are cysteine (Cys), tyrosine (Tyr), phenylalanine (Phe), glutamic acid (Glu), aspartic acid (Asp), proline (Pro), arginine (Arg) and glycine (Gly). You don't need to remember these names and codes; they are just given for interest. Note that the nitrogen in this terminal amine group forms four covalent bonds rather than the three shown previously, so has a valency of four. It also carries a positive charge. This is because one of the four bonds to the nitrogen atom is a pair of electrons provided just by the nitrogen atom. So, ownership of two electrons has changed to half-ownership of two electrons, numerically equivalent overall to losing an electron, so the nitrogen atom has a single positive charge. This type of bond is known as dative covalent.

**Figure 3.5** Primary structure of vasopressin. Note the highlighted sulfur–sulfur linkage between the two cysteine residues. This will be discussed shortly.

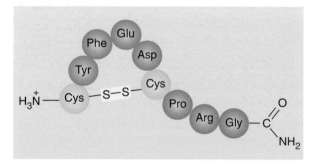

Almost all proteins fall into one of two classes, fibrous or globular proteins – each type plays a different role in the body.

### 3.1.2  Fibrous proteins

Fibrous proteins are generally used as structural material in the body. They are an important part of muscles, tendons, hair and finger nails. At the molecular level they tend to have many repeating segments of amino acids.

With such long chains of molecules, you might think that a sample of protein would be rather like a plate of cooked spaghetti, with all the chains entwined haphazardly, but this is not the case. For example, collagen – the most abundant protein in the body – is used to form the connective tissue that surrounds the bundles of muscle fibres and connects muscles to the skeleton. Each polymer chain in collagen is very long, containing about 1000 amino acid residues. The main repeating segments involve the amino acids glycine, proline and hydroxyproline (Gly, Pro and Hyp, respectively), although the exact make-up varies slightly from one polymer molecule to the next. Rather than being haphazardly entwined, the polymer chains group together in threes and coil around each other, rather like a rope. These ropes then line up longitudinally producing a highly structured system that forms strong connective tissue.

### 3.1.3  Globular proteins

Enzymes belong to the other class of protein known as globular proteins. These are of a fixed chain length and have a strict order of amino acid residues. Thus, all molecules of a particular globular protein are identical, which is not the case with fibrous proteins.

Each long chain polymer molecule of a globular protein has a specific job to do, be it digesting food, transferring information in the body or fighting bacteria. Only if it has the right sequence of amino acid residues will it be able to carry out this activity. Whilst the sequence of amino acid residues, i.e. its primary structure, varies greatly between one type of globular protein and another, in any particular type of globular protein the sequence is very specific to that protein.

However, a globular protein is not only characterised by its primary structure. Whereas in fibrous proteins several protein chains bundle together to make a strong fibre, in globular proteins it is the links between sections *within* a particular chain that are more important, leading to the joining of one part of the chain to another. Look at Figure 3.6, which shows a globular protein folded into one particular shape. The chain is forced to take up a specific shape by anchoring to itself at specific points along the backbone. Four sulfur–sulfur linkages (shown in yellow) like the one in vasopressin (Figure 3.5) are shown.

As you will soon see, this precise three-dimensional shape is necessary for the activity of the enzyme. Only this shape will do. The chain is held in this precise structure by crosslinks that are not random but built into the protein chain at specific points to do a particular job. The crosslinks hold distant parts of the primary structure close to each other. If these crosslinks are broken, the chain unfolds and takes up a random structure. The old structure cannot easily be reformed and the protein loses the properties that enabled it to function. When a globular protein loses its shape it has become denatured and loses its activity.

Another important contributor to the overall shape is the way that the amino acid sequences in the protein chain can coil into helices or into sheets (see Figure 3.6). The coiling and folding of sections of the chain enables functional groups along the chain to be close enough to each other to form the crosslinks.

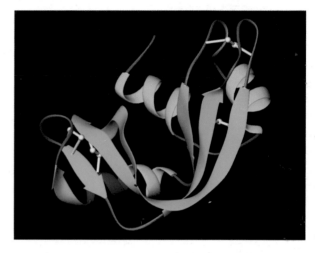

**Figure 3.6**   A 'ribbon' model of the enzyme ribonuclease. This globular protein, which consists of a chain of 124 amino acid residues, is used to break down ribonucleic acid (RNA) in the stomach. Most globular proteins are very long chains, and this is one simple way of representing them. The sulfur–sulfur crosslinks are shown in yellow.

## 3.2   Attractive forces: intramolecular (within molecules) and intermolecular (between molecules)

The crosslinks between different sections of the protein chain can take a variety of forms. One type is a disulfide link. This is two covalently bonded sulfur atoms and is indicated in vasopressin (Figure 3.5) by the —S—S— group and in ribonuclease (Figure 3.6) by the yellow sulfur atoms and the yellow bonds.

Apart from the covalent disulfide links, the other main type of crosslinking between different parts of the chain is hydrogen bonding, although other forces are often present, such as dipole–dipole attractions, London forces and ionic attractions. In this section the ideas on chemical bonding introduced in Section 1.8 are developed to explain what these interactions are and how they arise.

### 3.2.1  Covalent bonds

The two sulfur atoms shown linking the two cysteine residues in vasopressin (Figure 3.5) do so by forming covalent bonds between atoms in different parts of the chain. The amino acid cysteine has a sulfur atom as part of its side-chain. Two such cysteine amino acid residues in different parts of a protein backbone can be brought together to form a sulfur–sulfur bond (disulfide link) that links the two parts together, as shown in Reaction 3.3. There is really no difference in type between these covalent bonds and those anywhere else in a molecule.

$$\text{loss of hydrogen} \longrightarrow \tag{3.3}$$

### 3.2.2  Dipole–dipole attractions

You should recall from Section 1.8 that a covalent bond is a pair of shared electrons that holds the two bonded atoms together because the bonding electrons are attracted to the positively charged nuclei of both atoms. Now, it is not unreasonable to suggest that the nuclei of atoms of *different* elements, joined by a covalent bond, may attract the pair of bonding electrons unequally, after all the atoms of different elements will have different numbers of protons in their nuclei. If the atom of one element attracts them a bit more than the other it is said to be more electronegative. The result of this is that it acquires a small negative charge and the other atom acquires a small positive charge. This is shown in Figure 3.7a, in which the bonding pair is nearer to the atom of X than it is to the atom of Y. The symbol δ (Greek letter, pronounced 'delta') is often used to mean 'a small part of' so here it means a small positive or negative charge. For convenience, the style of Figure 3.7b is often used. Although the bond is not shown shifted towards the X atom it is implicit by the use of δ– and δ+.  Figure 3.7c is another common way of showing the same thing. The molecule is said to be a dipole or, put another way, it is described as a dipolar molecule. This is often shortened to just saying it is polar but, whichever description is used, it implies a bond between two atoms where differing electronegativity creates small opposite charges in different places in the molecule.

Atoms of many different elements can be represented by X and Y and they can be part of quite complicated molecules. The important thing is that electrostatic attraction between positively and negatively charged regions enables the regions to attract each other by intramolecular attractions. Other polar molecules can be attracted to these regions, resulting in intermolecular attractions between the molecules. These attractions are called dipole–dipole attractions, and are particularly important in protein chains where examples of the charged regions are the carbon atoms (δ+) and the oxygen atoms (δ–) in the C=O groups, arising because oxygen is more electronegative than carbon.

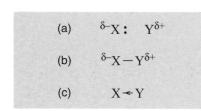

(a)    $^{\delta-}X \mathbf{:} \ Y^{\delta+}$

(b)    $^{\delta-}X - Y^{\delta+}$

(c)    $X \leftarrow Y$

**Figure 3.7**    (a), (b) and (c) Representations of a dipolar X–Y molecule.

### 3.2.3 Hydrogen bonds

Oxygen and nitrogen are two of the most electronegative elements and a special type of dipole–dipole attraction arises when they are covalently bonded to hydrogen atoms within a molecule. Remember that hydrogen is the simplest (smallest atom) element, the atom of which contains just one proton and one electron. As the bond forms between a hydrogen atom and either an oxygen atom or a nitrogen atom, the hydrogen's electron must move further away from the hydrogen nucleus as it will now be shared. Because it only has this one electron, this leaves the nucleus of the hydrogen atom rather exposed or, put another way, the $\delta+$ on it is relatively large. So, it follows that the $\delta-$ on the oxygen or nitrogen atom is also relatively large; overall the molecule is electrically neutral, so the $\delta+$ and $\delta-$ must be equal in magnitude. The result of this is that the molecule is very polar and can establish much stronger intermolecular and intramolecular attractions than normally found between dipoles. These stronger attractions are called hydrogen bonds and are a very important feature of the chemistry of living things.

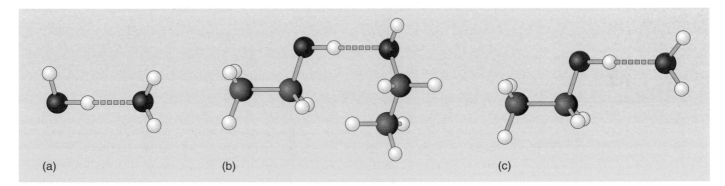

Typically hydrogen bonds form between the hydrogen of an —O—H or an —$NH_2$ group and an oxygen or nitrogen atom on another suitably positioned group. This can be a functional group suitably positioned on the same molecule or on a different molecule. Hydrogen bonds are not as strong as covalent bonds, so they are usually shown as dotted or dashed lines in pictures of structures of molecules. Figure 3.8 shows hydrogen bonds formed between (a) two molecules of water, (b) two molecules of ethanol (the alcohol present in alcoholic drinks) and (c) a molecule of water and one of ethanol. Compounds that are able to form hydrogen bonds to water often dissolve in it to make a solution, unless there is some other feature of the molecule that prevents it from doing so.

**Figure 3.8** Water and ethanol both have —O—H groups and so can form hydrogen bonds with like molecules (a) and (b) and with each other (c).

● Can you suggest an alternative way to that in Figure 3.8c by which molecules of water and ethanol can form a hydrogen bond to each other?

● The hydrogen bond could form between the oxygen atom of the ethanol and one of the hydrogens on the water molecule.

Figure 3.9 shows the four most common ways that hydrogen bonds can form involving hydrogen atoms (white), oxygen atoms (red) and nitrogen atoms (blue). These types are all very important when it comes to explaining how drug molecules are attracted to their targets.

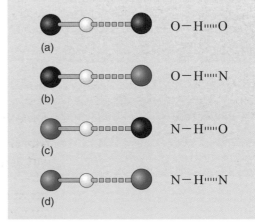

O—H⠂⠂⠂⠂O (a)

O—H⠂⠂⠂⠂N (b)

N—H⠂⠂⠂⠂O (c)

N—H⠂⠂⠂⠂N (d)

**Figure 3.9** The four most important types of hydrogen bond.

Not only do intermolecular attractions control the interaction between different molecules but, as they can form between like molecules in a single substance, it follows that they also control how that substance behaves. Take melting and boiling, for example (Box 3.2).

### Box 3.2  Melting and boiling

When a solid melts to a liquid it changes from being a rigid structure to a fluid one. The molecules are unable to move around relative to each other in the solid but are able to do so freely in the liquid. (This is one reason why diving into a lake is a different experience to diving into a frozen lake!) It is reasonable to suggest that there are more intermolecular bonds present in the solid than there are in the liquid and melting requires the breaking of these intermolecular bonds. This is why input of heat is required even if the substance is already at its melting temperature. Physicists call the heat required the latent heat of fusion because it does not cause a temperature change. Ice at 0 °C will remain as ice unless heat is made available. If heat is absorbed it breaks the hydrogen bonds between the molecules and the ice melts to form water, still at 0 °C. A similar situation exists when a liquid boils. Latent heat of evaporation is needed to provide the energy to further separate the liquid molecules as they pass from the liquid state to the gaseous state at the boiling temperature.

### 3.2.4  London forces*

**Table 3.1**    Melting temperatures and physical state at 20 °C for some hydrocarbons.

| Name | Formula | Melting temperature/°C | Physical state at 20 °C |
|------|---------|------------------------|-------------------------|
| ethane | $C_2H_6$ | −183 | gas |
| octane | $C_8H_{18}$ | −57 | liquid |
| tetradecane | $C_{14}H_{30}$ | 6 | liquid |
| eicosane | $C_{20}H_{42}$ | 37 | solid |

● Look at Table 3.1 and write a brief summary of the information it contains, focusing on the trends in the columns.

● The four compounds in the first column are all members of the homologous series of alkanes (end in –ane). The formula in the second column shows them in order of increasing molecular size. The third column shows that the melting temperature increases with increase in molecular size, from a very low value for ethane to a much higher value for eicosane. This results in only eicosane being solid at 20 °C.

● Given the information that hydrogen and carbon have very similar electronegativities it follows that hydrocarbon molecules are not polar. (They are referred to as non-polar molecules.) Neither dipole–dipole attractions nor hydrogen bonds should form between molecules of the alkanes. Does this suggest any problems in interpreting the trend in melting temperatures? Jot down your thoughts before reading on.

● You may have queried why the melting temperatures rise as the molecules get bigger or, indeed, why the alkanes can exist as solids or liquids at all. As the molecules are non-polar the discussion so far suggests there should be no forces of attraction between them.

* Sometimes referred to as dispersion forces or Van der Waals forces.

Clearly something must be wrong here. There must be some type of attractive force between the molecules, so the previous discussion must be incomplete. The forces yet to be considered are called London forces. They arise because the interior of a molecule is a frictionless environment and the pairs of electrons in the covalent bonds are able to vibrate to and fro within the molecule. Thus each molecule can acquire short-lived temporary polarities even if the atoms within it all have the same electronegativity. Each temporary, or transient, dipole is able to induce another temporary dipole on a nearby molecule, so therefore there will be transient dipole–dipole forces of attraction between molecules that are near to each other. These are the attractions known as London forces, named after Fritz London (1900–1954), a Swiss theoretical physicist. All molecules are able to form London forces, but these are very weak when the molecules concerned are small, hence the very low melting temperature for ethane. With bigger molecules there are more electrons generating the temporary polarity which is therefore bigger, so the London forces are stronger, hence the increase in melting temperatures. Figure 3.10 gives an impression of the relative sizes of the four molecules concerned.

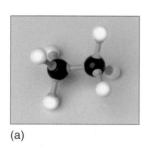

(a)

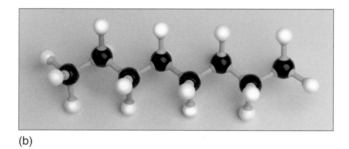

(b)

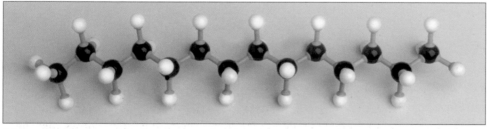

(c)

**Figure 3.10** Ball-and-stick models of molecules of (a) ethane, (b) octane, (c) tetradecane and (d) eicosane.

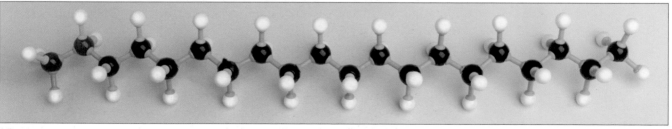

(d)

## Question 3.2

Although their molecules are about the same size, the boiling temperature of ethanol, formula $CH_3—CH_2—OH$, is 78 °C whilst the boiling temperature of propane, formula $CH_3—CH_2—CH_3$ is much lower at –42 °C. Why is this? ◀

### 3.2.5   Ionic attractions

Just as we saw an extreme case when the bonded atoms had the same electronegativity, so can we see the opposite extreme case when the bonded atoms have *very different* electronegativities. This is the case in, say, the compound sodium chloride (common salt, NaCl). Here, the chlorine is very much more electronegative than the sodium. So much so, in fact, that the bonding pair of electrons is not attached to the sodium atom at all. They reside entirely on the chlorine atom and there is no electron sharing in the way there is with a covalent bond. Effectively this means the sodium atom has lost an electron and the chlorine atom has gained it. Each therefore has a complete unit charge, +1 in the case of sodium and −1 for chorine. The formula is therefore sometimes written $Na^+Cl^-$, often NaCl, but *never* Na—Cl as this implies a covalent bond. These charged particles are called ions (pronounced 'eye-ons'), $Na^+$ being a sodium cation (pronounced 'cat-eye-on') and $Cl^-$ is a chloride anion (pronounced 'an-eye-on'). NaCl is known as an ionic substance. It is, perhaps, not surprising that sodium chloride is a high melting temperature solid. There are very strong forces of attraction between oppositely charged ions.  The specific ionic attraction shown in Figure 3.11 looks quite different to $Na^+Cl^-$ and will be explained in Section 3.5. Many ionic substances are soluble in polar solvents such as water because of the strong attractions between the ions and the dipoles on the solvent molecules.

To summarise, then, the forces of attraction between molecules, intermolecular attractions, or between different parts of the same molecule, intramolecular attractions, arise from the permanent or temporary displacement of the location of the electrons that are involved in bonding.

In order of decreasing strength these forces are: ionic attractions, hydrogen bonds and dipole–dipole attractions. Very roughly the magnitude of these attractions decreases by a factor of about ten each time as you move from ionic attractions to hydrogen bonds, to dipole–dipole attractions.

London forces arise from temporary displacement of the bonding electrons. They vary in strength, being greatest when the molecule is big but very weak for small molecules.

This completes our survey of the forces of attraction that can exist between sections of a protein chain. Figure 3.11 illustrates these.

**Figure 3.11**   The various types of crosslink used between protein chains in the molecules of globular proteins. The wiggly lines represent the remaining chain of amino acid residues. The zig-zag lines are a convention for showing chains of —CH$_2$— groups, used because, as Figure 3.10 shows, such chains are non-linear.

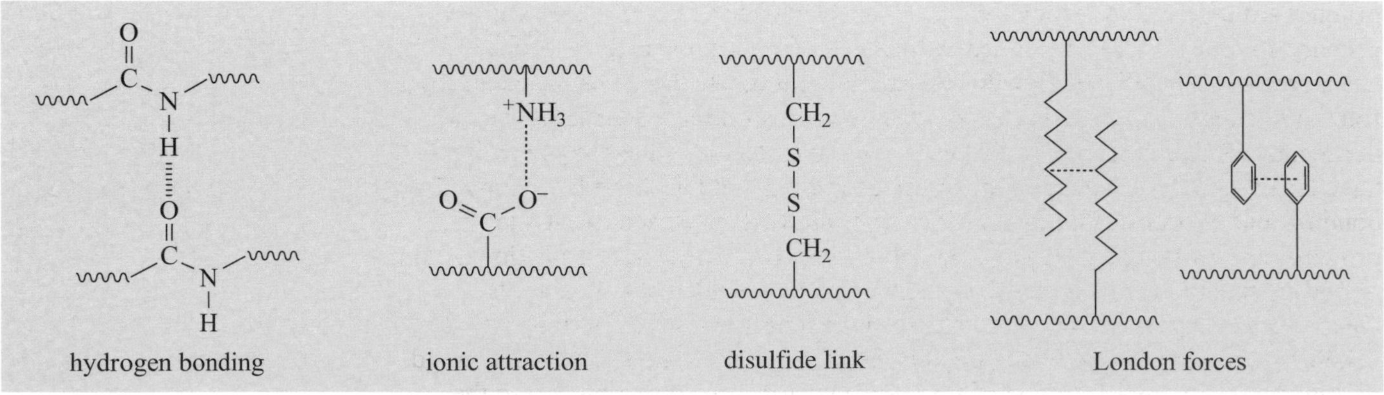

hydrogen bonding          ionic attraction          disulfide link          London forces

As you saw in Chapter 2, enzyme molecules need to have a very specific shape, so that the desired reactant molecules fit the active site but other, unwanted molecules, do not. It is the presence of the intramolecular attractive forces discussed in this section that makes this possible by ensuring that every molecule of a given enzyme has exactly the same shape, which will only allow the correct reactant molecules to bind by intermolecular attractions.

**Question 3.3**

Identify the opportunities for crosslinking between the side-chains on the protein segments shown in Figure 3.12. ◀

**Figure 3.12** Protein segments (for use with Question 3.3).

**Question 3.4**

Look at the structure for arachidonic acid, **2.10**, and suggest (a) what intermolecular attractions it could form to appropriate molecules of other compounds and (b) examples of groups there could be on the other molecules to take part in your suggested attractions. ◀

$$CH_3CH_2CH_2CH_2CH_2CH=CHCH_2CH=CHCH_2CH=CHCH_2CH=CHCH_2CH_2CH_2-COOH$$

**2.10** arachidonic acid

## 3.3 Enzymes again

Enzymes are globular proteins. They consist of a large number of amino acid residues, arranged in a specific order from one end of the chain to the other; the primary structure. All molecules of the same enzyme have exactly the same primary structure. One of the essential features of an enzyme is that its molecule has a precise shape, dictated by the primary structure, which causes the chain to fold up in a highly exact and reproducible way. This folding pattern, known as the secondary structure, means that every single molecule of the enzyme will have exactly the same convoluted pattern of folding, held in shape by hydrogen bonding and the other intramolecular interactions that have been discussed. If proteins, and particularly enzymes, are abused in some way, such as heating them or putting them in very acidic solutions, the carefully folded chain unravels. Once this has happened the order is lost and the enzyme loses its activity; it is denatured (Section 3.1.3). There are very many alternative ways in which it could fold up again and the likelihood of the resulting structure corresponding to the original structure is very low.

The importance of enzymes in facilitating reactions in the body becomes very apparent when an enzyme is missing. In Box 3.3 we look at what happens when just one enzyme is not being produced by a person.

### Box 3.3 Phenylketonuria

Phenylketonuria is a genetic disease that can lead to brain damage if not treated early in life. People with phenylketonuria do not make the enzyme that converts the amino acid phenylalanine into the amino acid tyrosine (Reaction 3.4). Tyrosine is an important amino acid for humans that can be obtained from the diet but if phenylalanine remains unconverted it accumulates in the body and reaches toxic levels.

- Examine the structures of phenylalanine and tyrosine in Reaction 3.4 and identify how they differ.

- The only difference is that tyrosine carries an —OH group on the benzene ring and phenylalanine does not.

Infants with phenylketonuria appear normal at birth, but if the condition is untreated, irreversible brain damage occurs by the age of one. Nowadays early screening identifies babies with phenylketonuria. By maintaining a diet low in phenylalanine, there is no build up of it in the body and thus the brain develops properly. People with phenylketonuria can thus lead quite normal lives.

The artificial sweetener aspartame ('Nutrasweet'), present in many low sugar 'diet' products, produces phenylalanine on hydrolysis so such products need to be avoided by people with phenylketonuria. You will often find the bottles labelled with 'Contains a source of phenylalanine'.

## 3.4 Back to aspirin

Although aspirin has been available in tablet form for over 100 years, its exact mode of action was only discovered in the 1970s, by John Vane (1927–2004). The work was of such importance that he was awarded a Nobel Prize for Medicine in 1982 and was knighted in 1984 in recognition of his lifetime's work in pharmacology, the study of how drugs work.

Chapter 2 ended with a schematic representation of the enzyme-catalysed formation of prostaglandin, and showed how aspirin prevents this by acetylating an —OH group in the cavity in the active site of the enzyme cyclooxygenase (COX).

So, how does the —OH group in COX arise?

Remember that COX is an enzyme, so is a globular protein, and as you have seen all proteins are polymers of amino acids. One of the amino acids that forms the primary structure of COX is serine, which has an —OH group on its side-chain (Figure 3.13). Its reaction with aspirin is shown in Figure 3.14; compare this to Figure 2.15 where we showed the same reaction in a slightly different style.

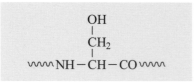

**Figure 3.13** A serine residue in a protein chain.

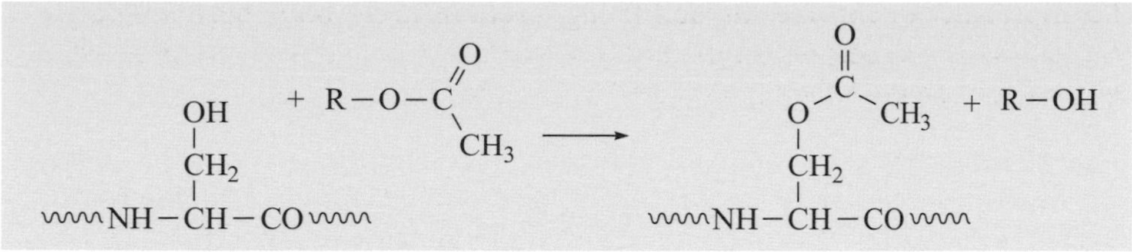

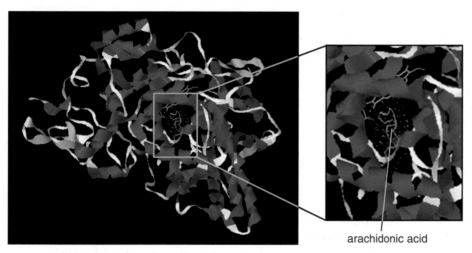

**Figure 3.14** The reaction of aspirin with serine in the protein chain.

The serine residue provides the $-CH_2-OH$ side-chain in the COX molecule for the aspirin to acetylate (Figure 2.15) and block access of arachidonic acid to the cavity (Figure 2.16). The serine in question occurs as the 529th amino acid residue in the primary structure of the COX chain.

Figure 3.15 shows an image of human COX, with an arachidonic acid molecule sitting in the cavity. The pink ribbons represent amino acid chains coiled into helices, whilst the yellow ribbons show the chains formed into pleated sheets. The grey area near the centre of the image is the arachidonic acid. This structure of helices and pleating is the secondary structure of protein, and is only possible with exactly the right amino acid sequence in the primary structure. An acetyl group within the cavity makes it impossible for arachidonic acid to be converted into prostaglandin. Pain relief results.

arachidonic acid

**Figure 3.15** A representation of a molecule of human cyclooxygenase (COX) enzyme with an arachidonic acid molecule in the cavity.

## 3.5 Some other pain relieving drugs – ibuprofen and paracetamol

It turns out that aspirin is not always the most ideal drug for the relief of pain. Part of the problem is that the acetyl group forms a covalent bond to the serine residue. This is a relatively strong bond that is not easily broken and so the reaction does not easily reverse. This means that a dose of aspirin takes quite a long time to lose its effect. Of course, this is not by itself a problem; in fact it could be an advantage – if only aspirin did not give rise to undesirable side-effects, e.g. bleeding from the stomach lining. Another type of prostaglandin molecule that is closely related to the prostaglandin that triggers pain is required to activate the formation of the mucous lining of the stomach, and its formation is also inhibited by aspirin, so regular use of aspirin over a long period of time can weaken the stomach lining to the point where bleeding can take place.

Since all drugs rely on changing the chemical reactions that go on in the body, it follows that it is very unlikely that any of them will be without unwanted side-effects. The search is always on for new ways to increase the specificity of our drugs, so that they bind only to the target site (so have no side-effects), achieve their purpose, persist for the appropriate amount of time and are then eliminated. In later chapters you will see how drugs to alleviate the symptoms of asthma have been modified over the years in an attempt to achieve these aims and how muscle relaxants, for use during surgery, have developed so that they are rapidly eliminated once surgery is over.

Aspirin is just one example of a non-steroidal anti-inflammatory drug (NSAID), providing relief from pain, inflammation and fever. There are many other pain-relieving drugs available 'over the counter' and on prescription and this chapter concludes with a brief look at two of them. Ibuprofen is a popular alternative to aspirin. Let's see what clues the structures of aspirin, **3.4**, and ibuprofen, **3.5**, provide about the possible mechanism of the activity of ibuprofen.

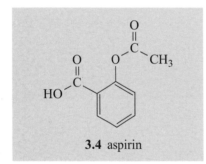

**3.4** aspirin

● Examine the structures of aspirin, **3.4**, and ibuprofen, **3.5**, and make lists of (a) their similarities and (b) their differences.

● (a)  They both contain a benzene ring with two side-chains, one of which is a carboxylic acid group (−COOH).

(b)  (i) The carboxylic acid group is joined directly to the ring in aspirin but is on a side-chain in ibuprofen. (ii) Ibuprofen has a large branched hydrocarbon side-chain, missing in aspirin. (iii) Aspirin has an ester group (−O−CO−CH$_3$), missing in ibuprofen. (iv) The two side-chains are in different relative positions on the two molecules.

● Now recall the molecular basis for the action of aspirin when it binds to COX to prevent prostaglandin synthesis and suggest whether or not ibuprofen could give *exactly* the same interaction with COX. Write down your thoughts before reading on. You should start by briefly recalling and noting down the steps involved in aspirin's action.

● Aspirin blocks the cavity in COX by acetylating the −OH on a serine residue. It does this by releasing the acetyl group from its ester side-chain (Figure 3.14). Ibuprofen does not have an acetyl group on an ester side-chain, so it is unable to carry out this reaction. Ibuprofen cannot, therefore, have *exactly* the same interaction with COX.

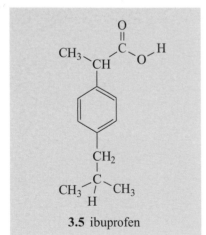

**3.5** ibuprofen

So how does ibuprofen exert its influence?

A comparison of the groups in its structure with those that we know can form various intermolecular attractions leads us to the carboxylic acid group and the quite large hydrocarbon group. The former could form hydrogen bonds with suitable groups on the COX active site, whilst the latter could form London forces. Research is still going on to find out exactly how ibuprofen binds to COX and it is likely that the last word on the subject is still yet to be written. However, one possibility appears to be ionic interaction between the —COOH on ibuprofen and the —NH$_2$ on the side-chain of an arginine residue in the COX active site. (Try a web search by putting 'ibuprofen COX' or 'ibuprofen platelets' into your search engine if you would like to find out more.)

Now look back to Figure 3.11, where one kind of ionic attraction is illustrated. On the basis of Figure 3.11 it would appear that —COOH and —NH$_2$ may not be quite the right groups for these attractions to occur. Ions, not uncharged groups are needed. However, one property of the carboxylic acid group is that it can form ions by releasing a hydrogen ion thus also forming a carboxylate ion; R—COOH $\rightleftharpoons$ R—COO$^-$ + H$^+$. The amine group, —NH$_2$, can also become an ion by reacting with a hydrogen ion, producing an ammonium ion: R—NH$_2$ + H$^+$ $\rightleftharpoons$ R—NH$_3^+$. (See Figure 3.5, where a similar ion exists.)

So, although at first it looks as if no ions are present, groups that can form ions are there. By losing a hydrogen ion the carboxylic acid group becomes an anion and by gaining a hydrogen ion the nitrogen atom becomes a cation. The two oppositely charged ions, one on ibuprofen and one in the COX active site, attract each other. This type of attraction between positively charged nitrogen atoms and negatively charged regions of another molecule (especially carboxylate ions) is very common in drug binding and you will see it again in later chapters.

Paracetamol, **3.6**, does not have the same mode of action as aspirin, **3.4**, and ibuprofen, **3.5**, and the basis of its action is still not fully understood. It has been known for some time that it influences synthesis of prostaglandins, but it is not an NSAID and, instead of acting at the site of a wound to suppress pain by blocking the active site of COX, it acts on the central nervous system. This is perhaps surprising, judging from its structure, as it is similar in many respects to aspirin and ibuprofen. One big advantage this gives to paracetamol is that it is a non-irritant, so does not carry the danger of causing stomach bleeding. This makes it an extremely popular drug for pain and fever relief, but its mode of action also means that it does not relieve inflammation – it is not an anti-inflammatory. Pain is registered by the brain but inflammation occurs locally.

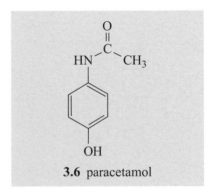

**3.6** paracetamol

## 3.6　Summary of Chapter 3

In this chapter you have found out that:

- Amines and carboxylic acids can react together to form amides.

- Protein chains can be formed when many amino acid molecules react together.

- A relatively small number of different amino acids (about 20) give a wide variety of proteins.

- The shape of a globular protein molecule is determined by its amino acid sequence and by the intramolecular attractive forces that exist between different parts of the molecule. These forces include covalent bonds, ionic attractions, hydrogen bonds, dipole–dipole attractions and London forces.

- The same forces of attraction, now called intermolecular attractions, enable drugs to interact with their targets.

- Each enzyme has a specific shape. It can only catalyse reactions of specific types of molecules because the molecules need to fit exactly into the active site, rather like a hand into a glove or a key into a lock.

- There is a range of NSAIDs, with similar but not identical modes of action.

- Other pain killers, e.g. paracetamol, are not NSAIDs but act on the central nervous system.

## 3.7 Reflection

Now that you have completed another chapter you may like to reflect in much the same way as you did at the end of earlier chapters. In particular:

- Were there any areas of the chapter that you feel you did not fully understand? Remember that the course is assessed by an ECA, not an examination, so from that aspect understanding the topics is much more important than remembering the detail.

- If there were any areas that you did not fully understand, did you make use of the 'How to get help' procedures?

- By now you should be becoming more familiar with ways of depicting molecules and equations representing reactions between them. This is not an easy skill to develop, especially if chemistry is a new subject for you.

# The Incas, Coca-Cola and a trip to the dentist

**4**

In this chapter we will look at how the stimulant properties, discovered by an ancient civilisation, of leaves from a plant led to an ingredient for the original Coca-Cola recipe and founded the development of local anaesthetics, widely used today in dental work and minor surgery.

## 4.1   The Incas

High in the Andes Mountains of Columbia, Peru and Bolivia grows a shrub, *Erythroxylum coca* (Figure 4.1). For at least 2500 years the leaves of this shrub have been known to have stimulant properties. Indeed, archaeologists have recovered several bags of coca leaves from the grave of one Peruvian ruler who lived about 500 BC. Despite the use of coca being limited to the royal classes and religious ceremonies, the Inca civilisation had high regard for it, and an ancient South American legend claimed that:

> … God's angels had presented man with the coca leaf to satisfy the hungry, provide the weary and fainting with new vigour, and cause the unhappy to forget their miseries.

With the arrival of the Spanish in 1533, the use of coca by the indigenous people became widespread, no doubt because the Spanish had observed that:

> … The herb is so nutritious and invigorating that the Indians labour whole days without anything else, and on the want of it they find a decay in their strength …

and therefore encouraged its use so as to extract more work from the indigenous population.

## 4.2   Coca-Cola

Surprisingly, coca leaves made little impact in Europe until the mid-19th century. Then in 1863 a Corsican chemist, Angelo Mariani, launched a tonic that was to become Europe's favourite drink, Vin Mariani (Figure 4.2). This beverage was an extract of coca in wine and as well as being a stimulant was claimed to be an effective painkiller, anaesthetic and remedy for flatulence. It was a runaway success, even receiving a special medal from Pope Leo XIII. Inspired by Vin Mariani, in the USA the pharmacist John Pemberton invented 'Pemberton's French Wine Coca'. This drink – sold initially as a headache remedy and stimulant – contained extracts of coca leaves, together with wine and extracts of the seeds of the tree *Cola nitida*, which contain caffeine (Figure 4.3).

In 1886, the prohibition of alcohol in the USA meant that the wine had to be removed from the recipe. Sugar syrup was used instead, and the drink became known as 'Coca-Cola' (Figure 4.4). Advertisements called it 'the intellectual beverage and temperance drink'. Two years later soda water replaced ordinary water, and in 1904 the coca extracts were removed and replaced with increased amounts of caffeine. This is essentially the form of Coca-Cola known today.

**Figure 4.1**   *Erythroxylum coca*, the shrub from which cocaine is obtained.

**EMILE ZOLA**

The Well-Known French Writer.

**EMILE ZOLA Writes:**

Vin Mariani--The Elixir of Life, which combats human debility, the one real cause of every ill—a veritable scientific fountain of youth, which, in giving vigor, health and energy, would create an entirely new and superior race.

EMILE ZOLA.

Never has anything been so highly and so justly praised as

**VIN MARIANI**

MARIANI WINE, the FAMOUS FRENCH TONIC for BODY, NERVES and BRAIN

*FOR OVERWORKED MEN, DELICATE WOMEN SICKLY CHILDREN*

Vin Mariani is indorsed by the medical faculty all over the world. It is specially recommended for Nervous Troubles, Throat and Lung Diseases, Dyspepsia, Consumption, General Debility.

MALARIA, WASTING DISEASES AND LA GRIPPE.

Sold at all Druggists.               Refuse Substitutions.

VIN MARIANI GIVES STRENGTH.

SPECIAL OFFER.—To all who write mentioning Leslie's Weekly, we send a book containing portraits and indorsements of EMPERORS, EMPRESS, PRINCES, CARDINALS, ARCHBISHOPS and other distinguished personages.

MARIANI & CO., 52 WEST 15TH STREET, NEW YORK.

Paris—41 Boulevard Haussmann; London—83 Mortimer Street; Montreal—28-30 Hospital Street.

**Figure 4.2**    An advertisement for Vin Mariani.

**Figure 4.3**    *Cola nitida*, the seeds of which contain caffeine.

**Figure 4.4**    An early advertisement for Coca-Cola.

Renewed interest in the stimulating properties of *Erythroxylum coca* leaves provided the encouragement needed to attempt to extract the ingredient(s) responsible for the biological activity.

## 4.3    A trip to the dentist

In 1860, the German chemist Albert Niemann successfully obtained pure crystals of cocaine which is the compound that is mainly responsible (but not solely so) for the biological effects of coca leaves. One of the first scientists to experiment with cocaine was Sigmund Freud. He quickly discovered the sensations that had long been known to South American Indians: euphoria, alertness, energy, and lack of appetite for food, as well as a marked anaesthetising effect when brought into contact with the skin.

There are plenty of scientists who would argue with Freud's perspective of mental function and many would challenge some of the conclusions he drew regarding the mood-altering properties of cocaine. However, his observation that cocaine's anaesthetising effect could result in it being a useful local anaesthetic was developed by one of his colleagues, Carl Koller. Chewing coca leaves makes the mouth numb and Koller noticed that pure cocaine invariably has this effect on the tongue. He had been searching for a local anaesthetic to use in eye surgery, so he tested cocaine first on a frog, then on a rabbit and a dog, then on himself. He found that, after trickling a solution of cocaine into his eye, he was able to touch the cornea and make a dent in it with a pin head without any awareness of the touch. This observation proved a landmark in the development of local anaesthetics. However, the growing awareness that cocaine had unwanted side-effects, particularly its effect on the brain, generated a search for drugs that would have a local anaesthetising effect but without the side-effects.

But where to start? In the latter half of the 19th century the molecular structure of cocaine was not known. However, it is now known to be **4.1**. The ring systems in this structure may look rather strange but they are quite common in naturally occurring molecules. Note that, just as some carbon and hydrogen atoms are often only shown implicitly in structures containing benzene rings (structures **2.4** and **2.5**), the other part of **4.1** adopts a similar style to prevent it becoming too cluttered.

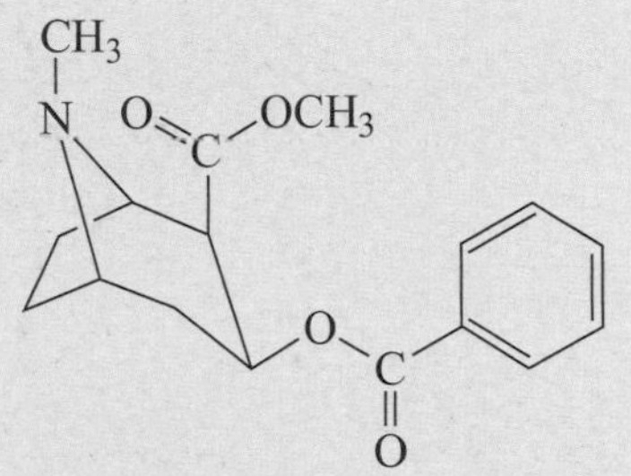

With knowledge of the structure of cocaine, today probably the first task would be to find out which of the structural features within the molecule are responsible for the biological effects. A logical approach is to test other compounds that are similar to cocaine but lacking one or more of the fragments or groups that might be responsible for its biological activity. If these compounds still have activity then it is probably safe to assume that the omitted fragments are not important biologically. However, if the amended compounds are not active then it is probable that the omitted fragments are important in bringing about the biological effect. This is a major strategy employed in drug development.

● Examine the molecular structure of cocaine, **4.1**, and try to identify the functional groups that are present. You may find reference to Table 2.1 or the bookmark useful.

● The functional groups are identified in Figure 4.5a. Their importance will be discussed shortly.

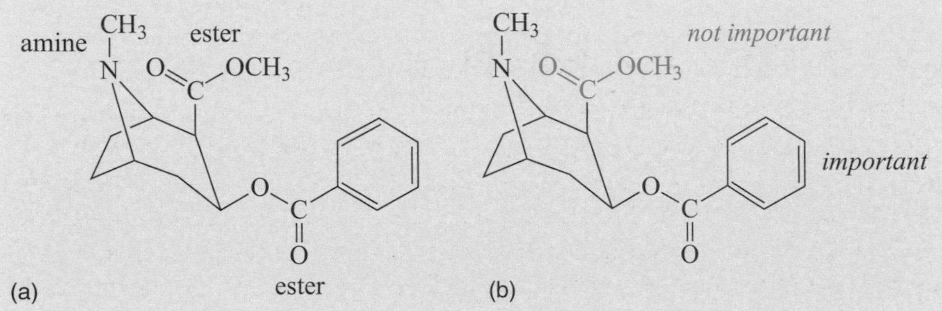

**4.1** cocaine

(a)          (b)

**Figure 4.5** The structure of cocaine showing (a) the functional groups and (b) the relevance of the ester groups to local anaesthetic activity.

By the mid-1880s it was appreciated that the hydrolysis reaction for esters, which you met in Section 2.5, broke the cocaine molecule into three fragments. These are benzoic acid, methanol (the simplest of all alcohols) and another more complicated alcohol that was also an amine (remember – a molecule can have more than one functional group in its structure); see Reaction 4.1. The formation of benzoic acid indicates that cocaine contains a benzoyl ester group. Reaction 4.1 shows this as a chemical equation. Make sure you can track the various groups carefully through this equation. We have colour coded the important parts to help with this. Remember that when an ester undergoes hydrolysis it reacts with water and forms a molecule of an alcohol and a molecule of a carboxylic acid.

| amine-containing fragment | benzoyl ester | | amine-containing ring system | benzoic acid | methanol | (4.1) |

### Question 4.1

In Reaction 4.1 the numbers of atoms of each element on each side are not equal (remember that atoms cannot be created or destroyed in chemical reactions). This is because the water molecules needed for hydrolysis are not shown. How many molecules of water does the equation need and on which side of the equation are they needed? (Remember that each ester group needs one water molecule for hydrolysis.) ◄

By making small changes to the structure of cocaine and testing each of them for local anaesthetic activity it was found that the benzoyl ester group, shown in red in Figure 4.5b, and the nitrogen atom were important, but the presence or absence of the ester side-chain shown in blue appeared to make no difference.

Further synthesis and testing of many other related compounds led to the discovery that the other part of the molecule – the rather complicated ring system containing the nitrogen atom – could be made much simpler without loss of anaesthetic activity. As long as the nitrogen was present, it did not matter whether or not it was in a ring. What did turn out to be important was the distance between the nitrogen atom and the benzoyl ester group. Most covalent bonds are approximately the same length, so an easy way of checking distances is first just to count the bonds between the two atoms.

● Look at **4.2** and **4.3** and count the bonds between the nitrogen atom and the oxygen atom (—O—) of the ester group.

| 4.2 | 4.3 |

● You probably didn't have much trouble deciding it is four, so the distance between the nitrogen atom and oxygen atom in each molecule is similar.

- Now look at the cocaine molecule **4.1**. How many bonds are there between the nitrogen atom and corresponding oxygen atom in the cocaine molecule?

- Again, it is four. This important similarity to cocaine makes it perhaps not too surprising that both **4.2** and **4.3** possess local anaesthetic properties.

Ernest Fourneau, of Poulenc Frères (later to become the industrial giant Rhône Poulenc), developed the compound amylocaine, **4.4**. This compound has a powerful local anaesthetic action, and it rapidly became a substitute for cocaine.

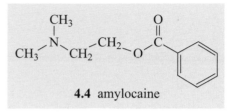

**4.4**  amylocaine

- Compare the structure of amylocaine, **4.4**, with **4.2** and **4.3**. What differences do you notice between them?

- Amongst other differences, amylocaine has one less 'spacer' carbon atom between the benzoyl ester and the amine group than there are in **4.2** and **4.3**. The important nitrogen to oxygen atom distance appears to be different.

It would seem, therefore, that the bonding arrangement need not mimic that in cocaine exactly. It looks as if just counting the bonds between the groups is not necessarily going to give a complete explanation. We can begin to see why this might be by carrying out the following molecular model activity.

### Activity 4.1   Comparison of cyclic and non-cyclic bonding arrangements in cocaine and amylocaine

Use your molecular model kit to make the structure shown in Figure 4.6, which represents the relationship between the ester group and amine group in amylocaine.

Keep your model of the partial structure of amylocaine intact, and make the structure shown in Figure 4.7 to represent the relationship between the same two groups in cocaine.

**Figure 4.6**   A partial molecular model of amylocaine to show the distance between the red oxygen atom of the ester group and the blue nitrogen of the amine group.

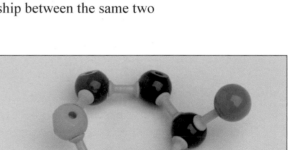

**Figure 4.7**   A partial molecular model of cocaine to show the distance between the ester group and the amine group.

Now see if you can manipulate your two models so that the oxygen atom of one model overlaps with the oxygen atom of the other and, at the same time, the nitrogen atom of one overlaps with the nitrogen atom of the other. Remember that atoms can rotate about single bonds.

When we tried this activity we found that one way to achieve this overlap of atoms is to arrange the molecules as shown in Figure 4.8. You may have found an alternative that still shows the nitrogen (blue) atoms and the oxygen (red) atoms coinciding.

*Note how the situation changed when we switched to working in three dimensions, rather than just counting bonds that separate groups in flat representations of the molecules.*

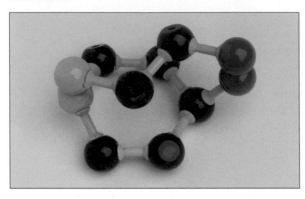

**Figure 4.8**   Comparison of the partial molecular models of amylocaine and cocaine.

Since many of the carbon atoms do not overlap in Figure 4.8, it seems that their positions are not important for local anaesthetic activity.

● What does this tell us about the relationship of the amine and ester groups in local anaesthetics?

● It looks as if it is not the exact *bonding pattern* that matters, but the *distance* between the two groups.

● Now use your model kit to see whether the sequence N—C—O (as opposed to N—C—C—O, or N—C—C—C—O) would be likely to give local anaesthetic properties (if the analysis above is correct, of course!).

You should keep your partial model of cocaine to help you answer Question 4.2.

● Your answer should be 'No'; the distance between the nitrogen atom and the oxygen atom is much too short.

Further development of local anaesthetics from cocaine provided procaine, **4.5**, better known as Novocaine®*, a powerful local anaesthetic, as you may well have experienced if you have ever had an injection of it at the dentists.

$$CH_3CH_2$$
$$CH_3CH_2$$ N CH_2 CH_2 O C

**4.5**  procaine

$NH_2$

The discovery of local anaesthetics from initial observations of the effects of cocaine illustrates clearly how a knowledge of chemistry is central to the development of new drugs: first, in the isolation and purification of active compounds from known remedies; second, in identifying features of the molecular structure that give rise to biological activity; and third, in generating new compounds with specific biological activity. This pattern is remarkably

*Note the convention of using a capital letter for the name of a commercial preparation containing a drug, but a lower case letter for the name of the drug. ® indicates that the name is a registered trade mark.

similar to that used in the discovery of new drugs for asthma relief that you will see in Chapter 6.

The progress from cocaine to procaine occurred without there being a full understanding of its molecular structure, and almost no understanding of how local anaesthetics actually bring about their biological effect. With the wisdom of hindsight it has become apparent that important parts of procaine (**4.5**) are one of the amine groups, some spacer $-CH_2-$ groups leading to the $-O-$ of an ester and a benzene ring.

## 4.4   How do local anaesthetics work?

An explanation of how local anaesthetics work requires some understanding of cell structure but even then it is not *entirely* clear, at the molecular level, how local anaesthetics achieve their effect.

### 4.4.1   Cells

All forms of life, from microscopic organisms to humans, use cells to divide into compartments and contain the chemical processes required for energy and for the maintenance and propagation of life. Cells are organised so that these processes can be carried out efficiently. Although cells from different forms of life have different characteristics, and even cells from the same organism can be very different, most cells have at least some features in common, namely a cell membrane and a nucleus (Figure 4.9).

At its simplest the cell membrane is a barrier that holds the cell together – some cells have a cell wall outside the membrane to reinforce this function. The membrane also ensures that wanted materials are allowed into the cell and kept there, while unwanted ones are allowed out and harmful ones prevented from entering.

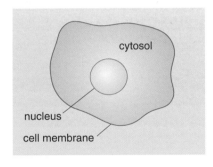

**Figure 4.9**   A simplified drawing of a cell.

The structure of the membrane is made up from roughly equal amounts of phospholipids and proteins. The phospholipids are molecules that have a long non-polar hydrocarbon chain (depicted as yellow wiggly lines in Figure 4.10) with a water-soluble polar group at one end (the blue circles in Figure 4.10). The proteins (orange in Figure 4.10) are embedded in this basic structure. You will meet the structure of cell membranes again when we look at how antiseptics work in Chapter 8.

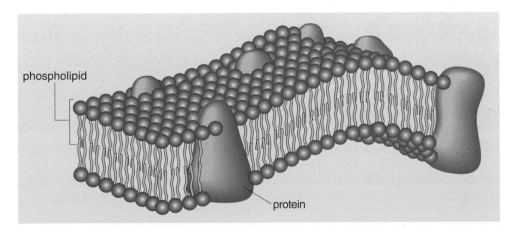

**Figure 4.10**   A representation of the structure of the cell membrane.

The membrane proteins have several functions: one of these functions is to recognise specific chemicals. The proteins respond to these chemicals and bring about a series of effects, such as allowing substances required for cell maintenance to pass through the membrane and enter the cell, or perhaps initiate a series of chemical reactions in the cell. This type of protein is called a receptor.

Other cell proteins that are found throughout the cell, not just in the membrane act as enzymes. The difference between an enzyme and a receptor is that *enzymes* enable and speed up (catalyse) the transformation of one chemical into another. *Receptors* respond to specific chemicals, but these chemicals do not react. Similarities are that they are both proteins and neither are used up when they are carrying out their function.

Within the cell lies the nucleus (Figure 4.9). This is where the nucleic acid, deoxyribonucleic acid or DNA for short, resides. DNA is the molecule that carries all the information for making all the other molecules that are needed for the processes that go on in the cell – in some ways it is analogous to the operating system of a computer. Most importantly, DNA also carries the information to replicate itself, which means that all of the information for the life of the cell is passed on when the cell divides.

As well as a membrane and a nucleus, most cells have other features that are important to maintaining life. These, too, are usually made up of lipids (a type of fat) and proteins, and another type of naturally occurring molecule – polysaccharides, which are related to sugars. Surrounding all of these features is a liquid called the cytosol (Figure 4.9) which contains water, soluble enzymes, proteins and the small molecules and ions required for the various processes of the cell.

Although cell structure is much more complex than the brief description given here, we are now in a position to identify potential molecular targets for drug action. First, there are the enzymes. The many different enzymes in a cell are each usually able to catalyse only one specific reaction, so interaction of a drug with a cell enzyme can stop the reaction that the enzyme normally catalyses. In Chapter 3 we showed how aspirin is able to block, or inhibit, the enzyme-catalysed process that leads to prostaglandin formation and the triggering of the pain response.

The second type of target is the receptors. Receptors operate in the presence of a particular compound by triggering a series of responses, so it ought to be possible to interfere with the way the receptor interacts with the triggering compound. We could, for example, design a compound that interacts more strongly with the receptor. This would prevent the usual compound from reaching the receptor and therefore diminish its effect. Although they are not the only targets at which drugs can be aimed, enzymes and receptors are two of the most important. They are certainly the most common, both when it comes to designing new drugs and in understanding how older drugs work.

### 4.4.2   Nerve cells – relaying the message

Nerve impulses are carried through the nervous system in two main ways. The first is by the release of a chemical 'transmitter' at the end of nerve fibres. After release, these chemicals pass to a neighbouring nerve cell and attach themselves to receptors. This type of information exchange is particularly important in the functioning of the spinal cord and brain, and is also the basis of signal exchange with glands and muscle cells.

However, we will concentrate on the other method of relaying signals, which is propagation along nerve fibres as a result of ions crossing the cell membrane. As they do so, they carry their positive or negative charges with them, so tiny impulses of electrical charge move into or out of the cell, altering the charge balance inside and outside the cell. It is by this means that signals are carried between tissue and the spinal cord and brain.

The cell membranes have channels through which the ions can travel, each ion having a specific channel. When the channels are shut no ions pass; when they are open, ions pass through. The cells therefore need some kind of switching mechanism to tell them when the channels should be open and when shut. It is well established that the principal mechanism is based on local changes in electrical charge, and that local anaesthetics can interfere with the ways in which charge alters. However, in this section of the course we want to discuss an additional property that local anaesthetics have, because it can teach us something about relationships between drugs and receptors.

It is thought that the chemical transmitter acetylcholine (pronounced 'ass-e-tile-ko-lean'), **4.6**, can influence the transport of Na⁺ ions through the cell membrane of nerve fibres, although neither its exact role, nor the origin of it near these sites, is known for sure. Some nerve fibres have a binding site that 'recognises' acetylcholine and can bind to it. It is thought that when acetylcholine binds to its receptor the receptor protein changes its shape to accommodate the acetylcholine molecule and this change in shape opens the Na⁺ channel to the passage of ions. Figure 4.11 shows this schematically.

If local anaesthetics are able to bind to the acetylcholine receptors, the transport of Na⁺ ions through the cell membrane is altered. Both cocaine and the local anaesthetics have molecular features sufficiently similar to acetylcholine that they can bind to the same receptor area. However, these molecules do not have identical shapes to acetylcholine, so their effect on the shape of the receptor protein is different. The channel remains closed off and ions are unable to migrate through it, so signals are not relayed. What is more, when a cocaine molecule is bound to the receptor, a molecule of acetylcholine cannot bind to it because its site is already occupied. So as well as having a different effect to acetylcholine, the local anaesthetic blocks the normal effect of acetylcholine. This change in the ability of the nerve cells to conduct electrical charges results in pain messages being prevented from reaching the spinal cord and brain.

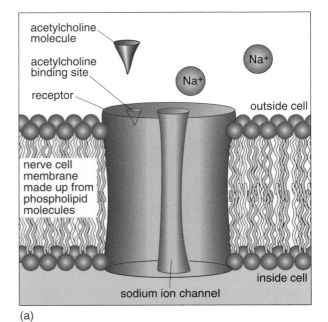

**4.6** acetylcholine

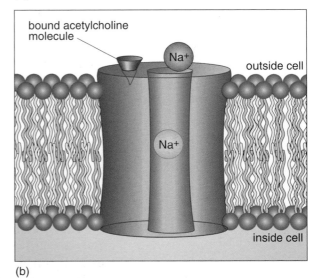

(a)

(b)

**Figure 4.11**  A schematic diagram of a sodium ion channel in a nerve cell membrane. In (a) the channel is closed so sodium ions, Na⁺, cannot get through. In (b) an acetylcholine molecule has bound to a receptor which allows the channel to open enabling sodium ions to pass through.

- Compare and contrast the structure of procaine, **4.5**, with that of acetylcholine, **4.6**. (a) Suggest what similarities might enable procaine to bind to the same receptor site as does acetylcholine. (b) Identify some differences between the two structures that might account for the fact that they have different effects on the ion channels.

- (a) They both have a nitrogen atom joined to a —$CH_2$—$CH_2$— hydrocarbon chain, which is then joined to the —O— atom of an ester group. (b) The other group on the acetylcholine ester is —$CH_3$, whereas procaine has a much larger benzene ring. So, this end of the molecule could be sufficiently different to cause a different effect on the ion channels.

### Question 4.2

Structures **4.7** and **4.8** are two potential local anaesthetics. Use your molecular model kit to decide which of them you would expect to have the greater local anaesthetic activity.

For **4.7** you need only build the fragment shown in Figure 4.12 and for **4.8** that shown in Figure 4.13. You will need to compare these models with the partial structure of cocaine you built earlier (Figure 4.7). ◀

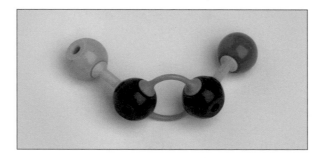

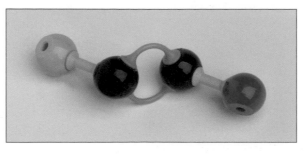

**Figure 4.12**   A partial molecular model of compound **4.7**.

**Figure 4.13**   A partial molecular model of compound **4.8**.

**Question 4.3**

What feature of the partial molecular models in Figures 4.12 and 4.13 was important when answering Question 4.2? (*Hint*: what did the double bond achieve?) ◀

## 4.5 Some final thoughts – pulling it all together

The quest of pharmaceutical chemistry is to discover or develop an arsenal of 'magic bullets', a range of drugs that can be specifically aimed at any one of the biological targets without straying off-target and hitting the others. These drugs, it is hoped, will have a precise mode of action, treating the illness or achieving an effect but not adversely affecting any of the processes involved in staying alive. This quest may seem hopelessly optimistic but it has had, and continues to have, notable successes, as you have discovered.

What then are the features of enzyme and receptor molecules that allow us to design compounds that can interact with them? As you may recall, both are proteins, made from the same amino acid building blocks (Figure 4.14). The general structure of enzyme and receptor proteins is formed by linking the amine group of one amino acid to the carboxylic acid group of another, with a peptide bond (amide bond), as shown in Figure 4.15. This continues until a giant molecule (polymer) of 50 to several hundred amino acids, linked together, has been formed. The precise role the giant molecule will have, either as an enzyme or a receptor, depends on how many amino acid groups are used to build up its structure, which of the 20 amino acids are used and, crucially, the order in which they are linked together. But no matter what their function, all of these biological molecules use a few simple forces both to hold together their own three-dimensional structure and to bind to other molecules. You have already met these forces in Chapter 3. They are hydrogen bonding, ionic attractions, London forces and dipole–dipole attractions.

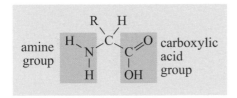

**Figure 4.14** General structure of an amino acid.

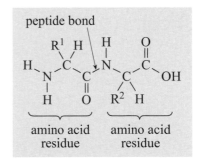

**Figure 4.15** Two amino acid residues joined by a peptide bond.

- To what kind of group in a drug molecule would a positively charged nitrogen atom (an ammonium cation) on the enzyme or receptor protein bind?

- Such a positively charged ion would need a negative ion to bind to.

Negative ions (anions) are often formed by carboxylic acids ($R-COOH$). One of the properties of carboxylic acids is that in aqueous solution they can lose a hydrogen ion, $H^+$, leaving the rest of the molecule, an anion called a carboxylate ion, with a negative charge, i.e. $R-COO^-$. (A good definition of the term acid is that it is a compound that can split up into a hydrogen ion and an anion.)

Reaction 4.2 shows this process. Note: (aq) in this reaction refers to an aqueous solution. Amines, the related ammonium groups where the nitrogen atom carries a charge of +1 (see Reaction 4.3) and carboxylic acids often occur in biological molecules so ionic attraction between positively charged nitrogen atoms and negatively charged carboxylate ions is a very important binding mechanism.

$$R-C\underset{O-H}{\overset{O}{\diagup}}\ (aq)\ \rightleftharpoons\ R-C\underset{O^-}{\overset{O}{\diagup}}\ (aq)\ +\ H^+\ (aq) \tag{4.2}$$

carboxylic acid                carboxylate ion        hydrogen ion

$$\underset{R}{\overset{H}{\underset{\diagdown}{N}}}\underset{H}{}\ (aq)\ +\ H^+\ (aq)\ \rightleftharpoons\ R-\overset{H}{\underset{H}{N^+}}-H\ (aq) \tag{4.3}$$

amine                    hydrogen ion              ammonium ion

Another interaction is hydrogen bonding between a nitrogen or oxygen atom on the protein and a suitable hydrogen atom on the drug molecule, for example an —OH group. The opposite interaction is possible, with the nitrogen or oxygen atom in a drug molecule interacting with a hydrogen atom in the protein. A third type of possible interaction is the London forces that occur between hydrocarbon chains and between benzene rings. All of these interactions are illustrated in Figure 4.16.

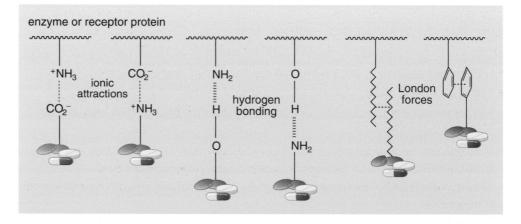

**Figure 4.16**   Potential bonding interactions between enzymes or receptor proteins and drug molecules, shown in a schematic manner.

Usually, binding of molecules to proteins requires a combination involving several of these interactions, using different regions of the molecule, rather than just one. Moreover, because the proteins have precise three-dimensional structures, the groups in a potential drug have to be correctly positioned in the molecule for the interactions to be possible. The challenge of drug development is to discover which groups to use and then how to position them correctly to maximise drug action. You explored some of the molecular implications of this in Activity 4.1. You will see further implications of this in Chapter 6.

Although we have concentrated on the cocaine to procaine (Novocaine) story, there is a range of other related products available. Before we leave the topic we will have a look at one of these. Clearly a useful feature of local anaesthetics is that they should be quick acting, producing a rapid numbing of the area for a sufficient length of time and then be rapidly released or broken down without causing unwanted side-effects. A widely used anaesthetic in dentistry is lidocaine, **4.9**, which is faster acting and longer lasting than procaine.

**4.9** lidocaine

### Question 4.4

Draw the procaine molecule, **4.5**, and place it beside the lidocaine molecule, **4.9**. Make brief notes that summarise the similarities and differences of the two structures and identify the important features that you think determine that lidocaine has an anaesthetic effect similar to procaine. You will find it useful to use your model kit to compare partial structures of lidocaine and procaine as you did for cocaine and amylocaine in Activity 4.1. ◀

### Question 4.5

List the main stages in the development of local anaesthetics from cocaine according to the strategy of drug discovery set out in Figure 1.3. ◀

## 4.5.1   A final final thought

Bearing in mind the link that has been suggested between tooth decay and over-indulgence in fizzy drinks sweetened with sugar, it is perhaps ironic that the natural product (coca) that gave us the original Coca-Cola also provided the lead to the drug that is widely used to reduce pain during dentistry.

# 4.6   Summary of Chapter 4

In this chapter you have seen how the strategy for drug development from a naturally occurring substance with some known effects on the human body has been applied to produce some local anaesthetics. You have seen that:

- Potential drugs, e.g. cocaine, can be isolated from plant material.

- Knowledge of molecular structure provides the basis for developing new compounds with potentially useful biological activity, e.g. amylocaine and procaine.

- Fragments of molecular structures can be compared using molecular models to identify shape relationships between atoms, or groups of atoms, in a molecule that may be responsible for the biological activity of the compounds concerned.

- The distances between some, but not necessarily all, groups of similar atoms are important in biologically active molecules, e.g. the N to O distance in cocaine, amylocaine and procaine.

- Drugs, such as local anaesthetics, may act on receptors to inhibit some aspect of the cell chemistry, e.g. $Na^+$ movement through the cell membrane.

- Drugs bind to cells by a variety of interactions, e.g. hydrogen bonding and ionic attraction.

- The process of drug development follows a path from the initially discovered compound, via knowledge of its molecular structure and an understanding of the molecular features that provide activity, to the synthesis of new compounds with optimum activity.

## 4.7 Reflection

Now that you have completed another chapter we suggest you go through the reflection process that you did at the end of the previous chapters.

This could also be a useful point to take a decision about which ECA to submit, if you have not already decided, why not discuss this with other SK185 students or others studying Science short courses if you are able to do so.

# General anaesthetics

**5**

In Chapter 4 you saw how local anaesthetics inhibit pain sensation in the region to which they are applied. Chapter 5 looks at general anaesthetics, which act on the brain to produce a state of unconsciousness and affect the whole body. Given all that chemistry offers to increase our comfort and wellbeing, there can be no doubt that the development of drugs for use during surgery would be high on anyone's list. Until the 19th century surgery was performed without a general anaesthetic but it is now taken for granted when surgery is required, there will be an anaesthetist available to render the patient unconscious safely and rapidly for the duration of the operation, after which recovery will be rapid, without any serious or long-lasting side-effects and with no memory of what has taken place.

So, how is this achieved?

## 5.1  The action of general anaesthetics

Although the exact and detailed mechanism by which general anaesthetics work is not fully understood, it is thought that the mechanism is somewhat related to the way that local anaesthetics function. You should recall from Chapter 4 that local anaesthetics are thought to work by changing the flow of ions into or out of the cell. This prevents the relay of the nerve impulses which the brain registers as pain.

It will probably come as no great surprise that the clue to how general anaesthetics work centrally on the brain lies in the detail of their molecular formulae. The formulae of some of them are shown in Figure 5.1 and models of their molecular structures in Figure 5.2.

|  |  |  |  |
|---|---|---|---|
| | $N_2O$ | | $CHCl_3$ |
| (a) | nitrous oxide (laughing gas) | (b) | chloroform |
| | $CH_3CH_2-O-CH_2CH_3$ | | $CF_3-CHBrCl$ |
| (c) | ether (diethyl ether) | (d) | halothane |

**Figure 5.1**  The formulae of some general anaesthetics.

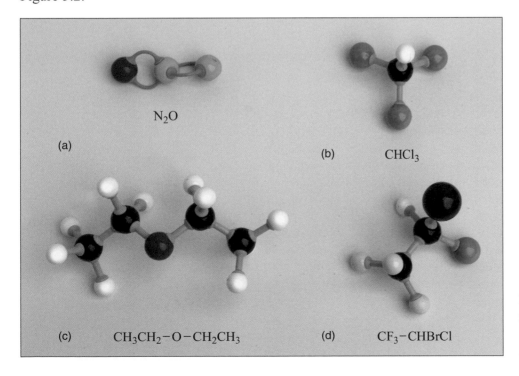

(a)  $N_2O$

(b)  $CHCl_3$

(c)  $CH_3CH_2-O-CH_2CH_3$

(d)  $CF_3-CHBrCl$

**Figure 5.2**  Ball-and-stick models of the molecular structures of the general anaesthetics shown in Figure 5.1.

There are quite significant differences in the structures, shapes and functional groups of these molecules. So, what does this mean? If you apply the ideas developed earlier in the course, where shape and functional groups were *very* important, you may well conclude that it is surprising that these four substances could all have such a common effect. After all, the functional group in ether (—C—O—C—) is very different to that in chloroform which contains the chlorine functional group (—Cl). The latter does have some similarities to halothane, but in halothane there is also a bromine functional group (—Br) and fluorine functional groups (—F). Certainly, none of the other formulae bear much similarity to that of nitrous oxide.

Therefore, it looks to be a reasonable assumption that any binding to cells that takes place is rather non-specific. All our previous work involved the attachment of specifically shaped molecules to specifically shaped binding sites to achieve their effect. Now reflect back to the range of intermolecular attractions that were involved in our previous discussions. They were ionic attractions, hydrogen bonds, dipole–dipole attractions and London forces (see Figure 4.16 for some of these).

Examine the structures and pictures of molecular models of the general anaesthetics shown in Figures 5.2 and 5.3. They do not contain any ions, so ionic attractions to the binding sites on cells are not possible. Neither can they form hydrogen bonds as the structures do not contain any —OH or —NH— groups.

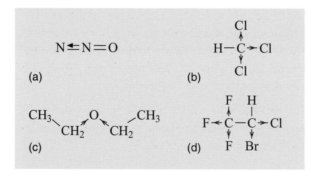

**Figure 5.3**    Structural formulae of some general anaesthetics. (Note: The bonding in $N_2O$ is different to the usual covalent bonding. This is another example of dative covalent bonding, first mentioned in Section 3.1.1. The arrow between the two nitrogen atoms indicates that *both* electrons in the bond originate from one of the nitrogen atoms, rather than one from each atom.)

However, they do all have covalent bonds joining non-identical atoms and this will cause some polarity within the molecules, as the bonding electrons will be slightly displaced towards the more electronegative of the two bonded atoms (see Section 3.2.2). We have shown this by arrowheads on the bonds in Figures 5.3b, c and d. The anaesthetic molecules will therefore be attracted to some extent to other polar molecules.

As with all molecules, they will also be attracted to non-polar molecules by London forces, albeit rather weakly as the anaesthetic molecules are not very big.

Now, the brain is known to be a 'lipid-rich' (fat-rich) medium and these lipids are largely non-polar. So, it follows that non-polar anaesthetic molecules should be attracted to these lipid molecules by London forces. Attractions between molecules of similar polarity can enable one substance to dissolve in another (chemists summarise this in the general rule 'like dissolves like') and the anaesthetic molecules are able to move into the cell membranes and dissolve in them. This causes the membranes to swell and expand and shut off the ion channels, interrupting the cell's ability to receive information by the movement of ions. This non-specific action is quite different to the specific action of binding to a specific receptor site. It is far more general and, indeed, there are many substances that are able to exert this influence on the brain cells to at least some extent. All that is needed is for the molecules to be non-polar and small enough to dissolve in the cell membranes in the brain. Even nitrogen gas is capable of this if the pressure is high enough to force sufficient nitrogen to dissolve. Fortunately the pressure needed is much higher than the pressure of the atmosphere, which is roughly 80% nitrogen. However, deep-sea divers can experience nitrogen narcosis* (loss of reasoning ability and manual dexterity – much like being drunk) because of this effect, if breathing a mixture of oxygen and nitrogen. The high pressure caused by the depth gives nitrogen a greater solubility in the brain cell membranes.

Having established a possible way that anaesthetics can act on cells in the brain we will now look at how the properties of the anaesthetic molecules enable them to get there. As well as needing to be chemically unreactive, to avoid harming the patient, it is no coincidence that many general anaesthetics are either gases or low boiling temperature (volatile) liquids that evaporate easily and become gaseous. This enables them to be administered by inhalation. In the lungs, they dissolve in the blood, which then transports them to the brain.

Blood, being an aqueous medium, is polar. Polar substances dissolve in polar solvents, but not in non-polar media. Non-polar substances dissolve in non-polar media, but not in polar solvents. (Remember 'like dissolves like'.)

● Can you see a problem here?

● It might be expected that molecules that are polar enough to dissolve in the blood might not be able to dissolve in the non-polar medium of the brain or, if they are non-polar enough to dissolve in the brain lipids, then they might not be able to dissolve in the blood.

The atoms present in the molecular structures of these anaesthetics underpin the similarity that they are all polar to some extent, but only slightly. It seems that the molecules are polar enough to dissolve by dipole–dipole attractions in the aqueous medium of the blood, whilst remaining non-polar enough to dissolve by London forces in the non-polar medium of the brain when carried there by the blood.

Another requirement is that the state of being anaesthetised needs to be readily reversible. Once the operation is over, and the anaesthetist stops administering the anaesthetic, the patient needs to return to consciousness as soon as possible. This is achieved if the anaesthetic molecules can evaporate easily and be lost from the

* Note: this effect is distinct from 'the bends' which are suffered only on return to lower pressure and are caused by nitrogen dissolved in the blood under high pressure coming out of solution as bubbles of gas when divers return to the lower pressures nearer the surface.

body, reversing the process by which they entered the brain in the first place. So overall we see a sequence of reversible processes: anaesthetic gas breathed in ⇌ absorbed through the lungs and dissolves in the blood ⇌ transported to brain ⇌ transfers to non-polar medium of the brain ⇌ affects the cell membranes, closing the ion channels, thus preventing communication with the brain and rendering the patient unconscious.

(Note the use of the same symbol, ⇌, as we used to indicate that a chemical reaction can go in either direction.)

This section concludes with a brief look at some of the compounds that act as general anaesthetics.

### Nitrous oxide

**Figure 5.4**    Nitrous oxide, $N_2O$.

Nitrous oxide (Figure 5.4) produces relatively shallow anaesthesia so was useful for minor surgery, such as dentistry, and was first used in 1844, by H. Wells, for this purpose. Although it is not usually used for dentistry nowadays, nitrous oxide is still widely used during childbirth as so-called 'gas and air'. When inhaled in small amounts it produces a feeling of intoxication, hence its popular name 'laughing gas'.

### Ether

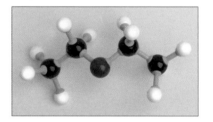

**Figure 5.5**    Ether, $CH_3CH_2-O-CH_2CH_3$.

Ether (Figure 5.5) was first used by C. Long in 1842 but is no longer used. It causes a high level of post-operative nausea and is highly flammable. Mixtures of ether vapour and air are explosive and, with the increasing use of electrical equipment during surgery, there have been a number of fatal explosions.

### Chloroform

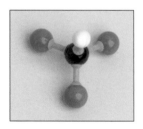

**Figure 5.6**    Chloroform, $CHCl_3$.

Queen Victoria used chloroform (Figure 5.6) during the births of her last two children. Chloroform is an effective anaesthetic and is not flammable, but it can cause liver damage so is no longer used.

### Halothane

**Figure 5.7**    Halothane, $CF_3-CHBrCl$.

The 19th century and early 20th century anaesthetics were far from ideal and by 1940 it was clear that some research to find improved successors was needed. This was undertaken at what was then Imperial Chemical Industries (ICI)* and, out of many compounds investigated, in 1956 halothane (Figure 5.7) emerged as an effective anaesthetic that met the requirements of not being flammable, not causing excessive side-effects and being rapid in action and recovery. It is still widely used today.

The molecular structures of two other modern general anaesthetics are shown in Figure 5.8.

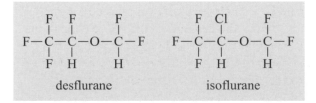

**Figure 5.8**    Two modern general anaesthetics, desflurane and isoflurane.

* Now AstraZeneca.

● What are (a) the similarities, and (b) the differences between the structures of desflurane and isoflurane (Figure 5.8)?

● (a) They both have a two-carbon atom fragment and a one-carbon atom fragment joined to an oxygen atom. By comparison to the structure of ether (Figure 5.1) you may have noted that both of these anaesthetics contain the ether group, $C-O-C$. Another similarity is they both have a $-CF_3$ group at one end and a $-CF_2H$ at the other end. (b) There is only one real difference and this is that isoflurane has one chlorine atom whereas in desflurane this is replaced by a fluorine atom.

A pattern is beginning to emerge. Some of the properties of chlorine will be discussed in Chapter 8. You will see there that an outstanding feature of the chemistry of the element is its unpleasantness, arising from its high reactivity. Fluorine is very similar to chlorine, but is even more reactive – they are both examples of the class of elements known as the halogens (others are bromine and iodine). Now, it is a good general principle that if an element is very reactive, once it has reacted the compounds formed are often very stable. This is precisely what has happened here and it is no coincidence that many compounds used as general anaesthetics have many carbon–halogen bonds in their structures. This makes them very stable and chemically unreactive, so they are not likely to cause harm to the anaesthetised patient. Their unreactive nature also makes them non-flammable. Look back to the structures of chloroform and halothane and compare them to desflurane and isoflurane.

As you might expect from the structural similarities, isoflurane and desflurane have similar anaesthetic uses with some minor, but nevertheless useful, variations in their effects. For example, isoflurane produces anaesthesia more slowly than desflurane, whilst desflurane results in a slightly shorter recovery time but is more irritating to inhale.

### 5.1.1  Recent and future work on the mechanism of action of general anaesthetics

Whilst it is always attractive to know all there is to know about a topic, this is unlikely to be achieved in areas as complicated as biological chemistry and pharmacology. Enquiring minds always want to do more research and develop more effective drugs. As they do so, new ideas emerge and displace or add to the previously accepted explanations. This is definitely the case with the story of general anaesthetics.

The account given here concentrates on the solubility of the drugs and the chemistry associated with their structures and there is no doubt that solubility is a major contributor to the mechanism of the action of general anaesthetics. However, recent research suggests that there may be more to it and it is likely that at least some, if not all, anaesthetics can target specific amino acids, or particular sequences of amino acids, within the proteins of the nerve cells in the brain. Much of this work has been made possible as techniques for genetic engineering have become available and have enabled, for example, mice to be bred that have specific amino acids missing or added to the cellular protein structures. This allows the effect of possible binding to specific amino acids or groups of amino acids to be investigated.

However, the *general* approach to drug development has not changed – detailed study of molecular structure followed by making small variations in it, followed by testing. The recent research findings on general anaesthetics are well beyond the level of this course but, if you want to follow it up we suggest a web search – targets such as 'molecular mechanism general anaesthesia' should lead you to some useful sites.

**Question 5.1**

Gaseous nitrogen, $N_2$, is referred to as diatomic because the molecule contains two atoms of nitrogen (N). The molecule has three covalent bonds (a triple bond) between the two nitrogen atoms. Draw its structure and make a model of it using three of the longer flexible bonds to make a triple bond, and answer the following:

(a) What forces of attraction are possible between nitrogen molecules and other molecules? Are they strong or weak?

(b) Why do divers only suffer from nitrogen narcosis during *deep* dives? ◄

## 5.2  A contribution from the forests of South America – the curare story

Curare has been known for hundreds of years as a lethal poison. South American hunters tip their arrows with it. It is such a powerful muscle relaxant that it usually results in death by asphyxiation, since breathing can no longer occur because of paralysis of the respiratory muscles. It decomposes during cooking, so is a convenient poison for killing animals for food.

In this part of the story on general anaesthesia, you will see how a study of the chemistry of curare and knowledge of the working of the nervous system has allowed the development of therapeutically useful drugs (curariform drugs) from curare, itself used as a muscle relaxant during surgery in the 1940s. Muscle relaxants are useful drugs because during surgery carried out under general anaesthetic it is necessary to prevent involuntary movements that could endanger the patient and health-workers alike. The use of a muscle relaxant to achieve this avoids the need to induce deep anaesthesia from which recovery can take a long time and be accompanied by unpleasant side-effects such as severe nausea. The ideal muscle relaxant should act during the operation and cease acting once the operation is complete. You will see how this property can be built into the curariform drugs.

### 5.2.1  Muscle contraction

A full treatment of how muscles work and are controlled is well beyond the scope of this course. However, it is known that one of the key features of the process involves acetylcholine, **5.1**, the 'trigger' compound for nerve impulses that you met in Chapter 4.

Acetylcholine is the transmitter responsible for relaying messages from nerve to muscle cells and thus exciting skeletal muscle, which moves limbs, the rib cage, etc. Acetylcholine achieves its effect by binding to receptor sites on nerve cells and triggering the chemical responses that lead to muscle contraction.

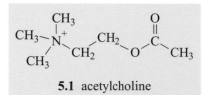

**5.1** acetylcholine

Figure 5.9 shows an acetylcholine molecule bound to a receptor site.

● What are the two types of binding attraction involved when acetylcholine binds to this receptor site?

● Figure 5.9 shows the positively charged nitrogen ($N^+$) of the acetylcholine molecule has ionic attraction for negatively charged (anion) groups on the receptor, whilst the oxygen atom on the ester end of the molecule is hydrogen bonded to an —OH group on the receptor.

A possible way of preventing muscle contractions by keeping them permanently relaxed is beginning to emerge. This could be achieved if there was some way of offering the acetylcholine receptor an alternative molecule that binds to it but does not trigger the same chemical responses in the nerve cell. It turns out that this is precisely what curare does, in a rather neat way. It contains a molecule (tubocurarine) that possesses two cationic groups and an attractive idea is that it binds to the anionic regions in two different acetylcholine receptor sites. Because each cationic group only binds to one part of each receptor, it does not trigger the same response as acetylcholine; furthermore it renders the receptor less available for binding to acetylcholine, so muscle contraction is not triggered – the muscles stay relaxed. This was proposed as a mechanism for the action of tubocurarine chloride (Figure 5.10), the active compound present in curare from which, following the usual strategy in drug development research, it was isolated and identified.

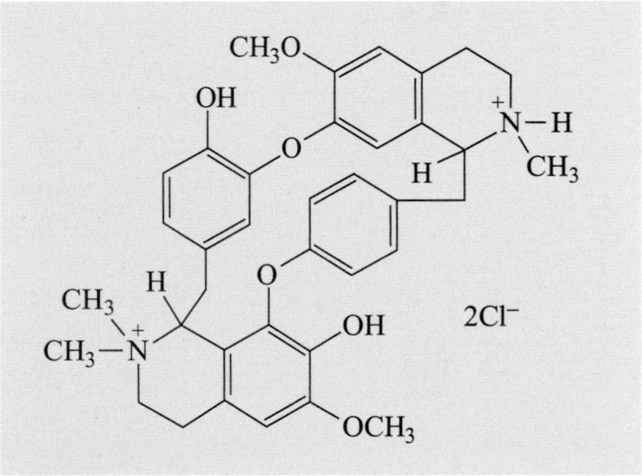

Note the presence of the two chloride ions in Figure 5.10. They are only really necessary to preserve electrical neutrality of the whole formula and will be omitted in subsequent formulae in this section as they are not involved in the binding of the molecules to the receptors. Ions that only have a passive role to play in a reaction are sometimes referred to as 'spectator ions', for fairly obvious reasons. For ease of reference in the discussion below, tubocurarine chloride will be referred to as tubocurarine.

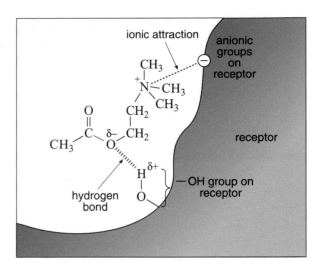

**Figure 5.9** Acetylcholine bound to a receptor site. The part of the receptor labelled 'anionic groups' possesses a number of anion groups, and therefore carries a negative charge on its surface.

**Figure 5.10** Tubocurarine chloride.

● Examine the structure of tubocurarine in Figure 5.10 and pick out the two cationic groups in the molecule.

● You should have found two positively charged nitrogen atoms (ammonium cations).

Although the structure of tubocurarine looks fairly daunting it turns out that it is just these two nitrogen atoms that are the important parts of the molecule for its action as a muscle relaxant. You can ignore the detailed structure of the rest of the molecule.

● Applying what you have already learned about the binding of drug molecules to receptor sites, what do you think is a crucial factor in the attraction of the nitrogen atoms to the anionic regions of the acetylcholine binding sites (Figure 5.9)?

- Obviously the fact that they are positively charged is important, but it is also essential that they are the correct distance apart to bind to two anionic regions.

Although the idea of binding to two anionic regions of different acetylcholine receptors was originally an attractive proposition it turned out that the distances in tubocurarine were wrong. Once the distance between the two nitrogen atoms had been determined (about 1.4 nm, or $1.4 \times 10^{-9}$ m), it became clear that the tubocurarine molecule could not bridge the much greater distance (9–10 nm) between sites on two adjacent protein complexes on the nerve cells. (If you have not met this style of expressing such small sizes before, you will find it explained in the *Maths Skills Booklet*.)

Some other binding mechanism must be involved. In common with what you have already seen with some other topics involving complex molecules, the exact mode of binding currently remains uncertain. However, recent proposals are that one of the nitrogen atoms of tubocurarine binds ionically to an acetylcholine receptor's anionic region, whilst the other nitrogen atom binds to a negatively charged cysteine residue in the protein (see Section 3.1.1) which is located about 1.2 nm from the anionic region. It seems that this slight difference in distance (1.2 nm instead of 1.4 nm) may not be important.

In spite of this uncertainty there is much evidence that the two nitrogens and the distance between them are very important. This is confirmed by the structures of other drugs (curariform drugs) that have been developed for use during surgery, using tubocurarine as the lead compound. The development of one of these, suxamethonium, is a classic example of the general strategy for drug discovery described in Section 1.2.

- Starting at one of the nitrogen atoms in tubocurarine chloride (Figure 5.10), count the number of other atoms that separate it from the other nitrogen atom, by the shortest route that you can find (you will probably discover there are two possible routes).

- The number of atoms is 10.

- Assuming that *only* the two ammonium nitrogen atoms and the distance between them are important, suggest the simplest partial structure, i.e. just the backbone chain, that might be capable of achieving the same effect as tubocurarine chloride.

- A good place to start would be $^+N-C-C-C-C-C-C-C-C-C-C-N^+$.

- Now add enough hydrogen atoms to keep the valencies of all the carbons and the two nitrogens correct.

- You should now have the structure:

$$^+NH_3-CH_2-CH_2-CH_2-CH_2-CH_2-CH_2-CH_2-CH_2-CH_2-CH_2-NH_3{}^+$$

For convenience this can be abbreviated to $^+NH_3-(CH_2)_{10}-NH_3{}^+$.

$$(CH_3)_3N^+-(CH_2)_{10}-N^+(CH_3)_3 \quad 2Cl^-$$

**5.2** decamethonium

This line of thinking led researchers to the compound decamethonium, **5.2**. This molecule has the same distance between two positively charged nitrogen atoms as tubocurarine. The two chloride anions preserve electrical neutrality.

When tested, decamethonium turned out to be a very powerful muscle relaxant and was evidence in support of the role of the two nitrogen atoms and the distance between them. This represented a triumph for pharmaceutical chemists. However, the interaction between decamethonium and the receptor is not quite the same as for curare and the receptor. Decamethonium does have unwanted side-effects. It is inferior to curare for general use and finds little application today. This outcome is not unusual in drug development – the first synthetic analogue of a naturally occurring lead compound is rarely the one of final choice. So, further research and development was needed.

Experiments in searching for a better drug examined how critical the value of $n$ is in the formula:

$$(CH_3)_3N^+-(CH_2)_n-N^+(CH_3)_3$$

● If the binding to receptor sites proceeds as we have suggested, how do you expect the binding activity to vary as the chain length is increased from $n = 2$ to $n = 20$?

● From the previous discussion, we might expect the greatest activity when $n = 10$. However, chains of $-CH_2-$ groups are very flexible, because the atoms can rotate about single bonds, so it is possible that molecules with other values for $n$ would also fit the receptor sites.

This prediction more or less summarises what actually happens. Activity starts at about $n = 5$ and increases to a maximum at about $n = 9$ to $n = 12$. Above $n = 12$ the activity decreases again because the extra chain length means it would need to be increasingly folded in order to fit the sites. As the chain length increases above $n = 12$, the exact folding pattern to create the required distance between the nitrogen atoms becomes less and less probable. Regardless of the value of $n$, none of the new compounds gave an improved drug, so further modification was needed.

### Question 5.2

The argument in the previous paragraph concerning the longer chain being very unlikely to be in the exact shape to fit the receptor sounds reasonable enough. However, enzymes and receptor proteins have chains of many hundreds of amino acid residues and by a similar argument it could be considered very unlikely that they would adopt the precise shape needed to be able to do their job in the cell. Why is it that they can, and do, adopt exactly the same shape for every molecule of a particular enzyme or receptor, but identical long chains of $-CH_2-$ groups do not give rise to identically shaped molecules? ◀

One problem with curare and decamethonium is that their effects are long lasting. This is fine when hunting in South American forests or repelling the 16th century conquistadors, but not for muscle relaxation during surgery! Action should cease as soon as possible after the operation is complete. Attention was therefore turned to ways of designing a drug that could have a shorter period of action.

The problem was resolved by looking at what happens to acetylcholine. Removal of acetylcholine from the receptor site is carried out by enzyme-catalysed hydrolysis of the ester group in the molecule. The bond shown in red in Figure 5.9 (and in Reaction 5.1) is broken and the molecule is divided into two parts which are released from the receptor, allowing the muscle to relax. The enzyme involved is acetylcholinesterase. It goes without saying that the speed of these muscle reactions must be very rapid – just imagine all the chemistry going on as various muscles contract and relax when we raise a cup of tea to our lips! If there was *no* pathway by which acetylcholine is removed from the receptor, the muscles would rapidly end up in a state of permanent contraction* and normal movement would cease.

The enzyme-catalysed hydrolysis of acetylcholine (Reaction 5.1) can be made use of, if we can find a way of modifying the structure of decamethonium, **5.2**, so that acetylcholinesterase mistakes it for acetylcholine and hydrolyses it.

$$CH_3-\overset{\overset{\displaystyle O}{\|}}{C}-O-CH_2-CH_2-\overset{\overset{\displaystyle CH_3}{+|}}{\underset{\underset{\displaystyle CH_3}{|}}{N}}-CH_3 \; + \; H_2O \; = \; CH_3-\overset{\overset{\displaystyle O}{\diagup\!\!\diagup}}{\underset{\underset{\displaystyle O-H}{\diagdown}}{C}} \; + \; HO-CH_2-CH_2-\overset{\overset{\displaystyle CH_3}{+|}}{\underset{\underset{\displaystyle CH_3}{|}}{N}}-CH_3 \qquad (5.1)$$

- What is the feature of the acetylcholine molecule that facilitates its hydrolysis by acetylcholinesterase, and hence its removal from the active site?

- It is the presence of the ester group.

- How could the structure of decamethonium be modified so that it might undergo the same reaction?

- It would seem reasonable to try inserting some ester groups into the hydrocarbon chain, whilst retaining the same distance between the nitrogen atoms, and hope that acetylcholinesterase mistakes the molecule for acetylcholine.

After much experimentation, an effective compound was developed which has a shorter duration of action than decamethonium, with fewer side-effects. The compound is suxamethonium, **5.3**. It would seem that there is sufficient similarity between suxamethonium and acetylcholine for the active site (binding site) on the acetylcholinesterase to fit the suxamethonium molecule and catalyse its hydrolysis, thus halting its muscle-relaxing effect.

$$(CH_3)_3\overset{+}{N}-CH_2-CH_2-O-\overset{\overset{\displaystyle O}{\|}}{C}-CH_2-CH_2-\overset{\overset{\displaystyle O}{\|}}{C}-O-CH_2-CH_2-\overset{+}{N}(CH_3)_3$$

**5.3** suxamethonium

### Activity 5.1

Try making partial molecular models of just the backbone chain (i.e. N to N) of decamethonium and suxamethonium and check that the chains can be manipulated so that the nitrogen atoms are superimposable, so are indeed both able to fit onto the same nerve cell receptors.

---

* The nerve poison, *Sarin*, achieves its effect by blocking the action of acetylcholinesterase so that the victim's muscles are kept in a constant state of contraction – the reverse effect to curare, but just as deadly.

● What are the similarities between the molecular structures of suxamethonium, **5.3**, and acetylcholine, **5.1**?

● Both have a positively charged nitrogen atom carrying three methyl groups, separated from an ester group by $-CH_2-CH_2-$.

So, application of the general strategy for drug discovery took a naturally occurring lead compound and identified the essential aspects of its molecular structure. Knowledge, sometimes incomplete, of its mode of action then enabled the design of synthetic replacements, at first inferior to the lead compound, but eventually superior because its reduced time of action made it more useful as a muscle relaxant during surgery.

We will conclude this section here – from the 1950s onwards there has been a great deal more research than we have described, in the quest for muscle relaxant drugs with improved performance. The structures and mode of action of other compounds that have been developed bear a great deal of similarity to those we have discussed. If you want to follow up some of these compounds you could try web searches for 'pancuronium bromide' and 'atracurium'. You will find they share the same general molecular structure that we have discussed, namely two positively charged nitrogen atoms, a carbon chain separating them and the inclusion of groups to aid removal of the drug.

**Question 5.3**

Look back to the equation for the hydrolysis of acetylcholine (Reaction 5.1) and, by analogy, write out an equation for the hydrolysis of suxamethonium, **5.3**. ◀

**Question 5.4**

Why does curare have an almost permanent paralysing effect on the muscles? ◀

## 5.3  Summary of Chapter 5

In this chapter you have found out that:

● General anaesthetics achieve their effect by acting on the brain cell membranes, closing the ion channels and so preventing transmission of signals.

● The molecules of general anaesthetics need to have some polarity, so they can dissolve in the aqueous medium of the blood. They must not be too polar, as they also need to dissolve in the non-polar medium of the brain.

● It is important that involuntary contraction of muscle is avoided during surgery. This is achieved by using drugs related to curare, to bind to the acetylcholine receptors on nerve cells and block their action.

● Post-operative removal of the muscle relaxants can be achieved by designing them so that acetylcholinesterase is able to catalyse hydrolysis of ester groups within their molecules.

## 5.4 Reflection

By now you will be used to the process of reflecting back over what you have achieved.

It would be useful here to consider similarities between the different topic areas that we have discussed so far in the course. By now a familiar picture should be emerging of:

- lead compounds such as tubocurarine being adapted to produce useful drugs, e.g. suxamethonium.
- the similarities in the mode of action of the drugs. (Think about how intermolecular forces enable them to bind to an active site, making it unavailable for its normal function.)

# From herbal remedies to asthma drugs

6

In this chapter it becomes apparent that having a clear picture of molecular structure is invaluable to the logical development of compounds with specific biological activity. This story follows the stages in the development of the drugs salbutamol and salmetrol, which are used to relieve the symptoms of asthma, a serious respiratory disease, often arising from allergies, and accompanied by laboured breathing, chest constriction and coughing. The story begins with *ma huang*, a herb that has been used in Chinese medicine since around 3100 BC.

## 6.1  Herbal remedies

In 1596 AD, Kang Mu, a Chinese apothecary, claimed that *ma huang* – which consists of the dried, young branches of several *Ephedra* species (Figure 6.1) – reduced fever, improved circulation, induced sweating and eased coughing. Indeed an aqueous extract of the herb, produced by boiling the plant in water, can be shown to raise blood pressure, increase heart rate, constrict the blood vessels of the kidneys and bring about a widening (dilation) of the bronchial airways. A pure compound, ephedrine, **6.1**, can be isolated from the original aqueous extract, and this became the lead compound for a development programme that produced our modern treatments for asthma.

Ephedrine on its own has the power to dilate the airways of the respiratory tract, and this discovery rapidly led to ephedrine being used as a treatment for asthma. Unfortunately, an undesirable side-effect is its ability to raise blood pressure significantly. The herb *ma huang* itself does not raise blood pressure so markedly because it contains other compounds, one of which – called pseudoephedrine – actually reduces the heart rate and lowers blood pressure.

To a chemist, pseudoephedrine and ephedrine are related molecules in that they contain the same number and same types of atoms. If we draw their structural formulae in the abbreviated style used until now, their structures look identical. Structure **6.1** can represent the structure of both ephedrine and pseudoephedrine, so it is interesting that they should have such different effects in the body; one raising blood pressure, the other lowering it.

The subtle difference between these two compounds lies in the way their atoms are arranged slightly differently in space. This becomes apparent if we study models of the two compounds (Figure 6.2). The carbon atoms immediately attached to the benzene rings in these two compounds have the —H and —OH groups arranged in the opposite sense. So we need a way of showing this on paper and depicting them so that the way the groups are arranged in space is indeed different.

**6.1** ephedrine
(and pseudoephedrine)

**Figure 6.1**   One of the ephedrine-containing species of *Ephedra* or *ma huang*.

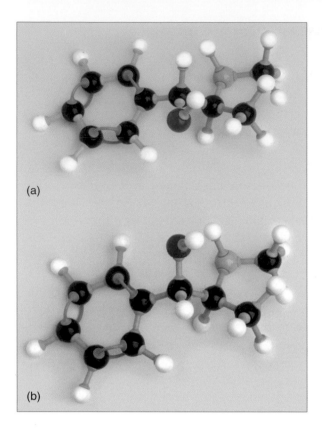

**Figure 6.2** Models of (a) ephedrine and (b) pseudoephedrine.

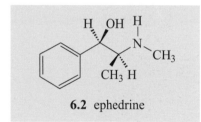

**6.2** ephedrine

Take a look at **6.1**; remember that as such it represents both pseudoephedrine and ephedrine. What we'd like is a method that shows, as we look at the molecule, how certain groups appear to be coming towards us, while others appear to be going away from us. Such a structure for ephedrine, **6.2**, uses a solid wedge symbol for groups coming towards us (the —OH and —CH₃), and a dashed wedge symbol for those going away from us (the two —H atoms).

● Look carefully at Figure 6.2a and **6.2** and then draw an equivalent structure for pseudoephedrine (Figure 6.2b).

● The only difference between ephedrine, **6.2**, and pseudoephedrine is the direction of the —OH and —H in space. See **6.3**.

We shall use this notation from now on whenever the precise three-dimensional spatial arrangement of atoms is important.

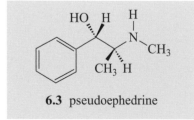

**6.3** pseudoephedrine

Biological systems experience these two substances as each having their own distinct properties and respond differently to each. This is a classic example of how isolating a pure compound from a herbal remedy can lead to a drug that has a different biological activity, simply because the herbal remedy contains several compounds with differing activities. In this case the biological effect of pseudoephedrine counteracts to some extent that of ephedrine, thus avoiding the unwanted side-effects of any one form of the compound.

Clearly we need to refine the search for an effective asthma drug by considering the shape of molecules.

**90**

## 6.2   Molecules and handedness

Except in the finest detail, our hands are mirror images of each other. They have the same features and same shape yet they are not identical. If you put one hand palm down flat on a table and then place the other hand palm down on top, it is obvious that you cannot imagine them arranged such that all the features of one hand occupy *exactly* the same positions in space as those of the other hand. If you hold your left hand in front of a mirror what you see in the mirror is the same as if you could hold your right hand *behind* the mirror and still see it.

Our hands are therefore not perfectly superimposable; they are in fact mirror images of each other. We say that they are non-superimposable mirror images. It may come as a surprise to learn that certain molecules have this property of 'handedness' too. Molecular handedness arises because of the way four atoms, or groups of atoms, can be arranged around a tetrahedral carbon atom. We considered the tetrahedral shape of methane, the simplest of carbon compounds, in Sections 1.6 and 1.8.1. Look back there if you need to review this topic.

In the next activity we explore molecular handedness using your model kit.

### Activity 6.1

To explore this topic further make two models, as shown in Figure 6.3. Each model represents a carbon atom surrounded by four atoms or groups, two of which are identical.

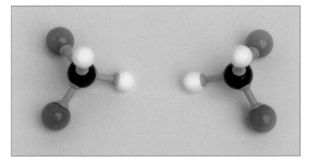

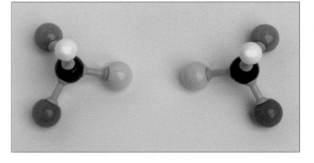

**Figure 6.3**   Models of a carbon atom surrounded by four atoms or groups, two of which are the same.

**Figure 6.4**   Models of a carbon atom surrounded by four different atoms or groups.

●  Can you determine whether or not the models you have made are identical?

●  You should be able to manipulate them so that each atom or group occupies exactly the same position in space. If you can, then obviously they are identical.

Now, use the model kit to make two further models like those in Figure 6.4. Notice that this time all of the groups around the carbon atom are different.

The models in Figure 6.4 have been arranged to help you see that they are mirror images of each other. But are they identical? Try to manipulate the models so that the groups occupy exactly the same position in space. You should find that it is impossible to achieve. The models will never be superimposable.

This is a general result; whenever four different atoms or groups surround a tetrahedral carbon atom there are always *two* ways of arranging the groups around the carbon atom. This means it is possible to obtain molecules that are, like our hands, identical in every respect except that they are mirror images of each other. Carbon atoms bonded to four different groups are said to be chiral (pronounced 'kigh-ral'), derived from the Greek word for hand. The two mirror image compounds are called stereoisomers. You were introduced to isomers in Section 2.6, but here we are focusing on the type of isomer that is concerned with the three-dimensional shape of molecules. Until quite recently, the methods used to synthesise drugs in the laboratory usually produced both stereoisomers. However, stereoisomers often bring about different biological responses, which may be the reason why some drugs have side-effects: one stereoisomer may be beneficial whilst the other is harmful. Sometimes, it is only one stereoisomer that is active while the other has no biological effect. In this situation, to use methods that make both stereoisomers would be wasteful. Not surprisingly, therefore, a lot of effort is now being expended in devising methods that produce only the useful stereoisomer, presenting chemists with many new challenges. The chemistry involved can be quite complicated and is beyond the scope of this course.

## 6.3   The search continues

The scarcity of *ma huang* and undesirable side-effects of ephedrine in treating asthma led to a drive to synthesise an effective substitute.

● Study the structure of ephedrine, **6.2**, and based on what you have studied so far, try to identify four structural fragments that might contribute to its biological activity.

● Ephedrine contains a benzene ring, an alcohol group, an amine group, and what is known as a branching methyl group (Figure 6.5).

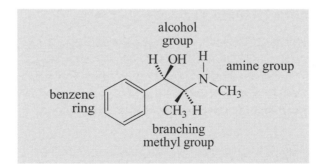

**Figure 6.5**   The structural fragments of ephedrine.

As we discovered with cocaine, when it is unclear which features of a compound's structure confer its biological activity, the best way forward is to make simpler substances which contain only two or three of these features, but preserve the shape and test them for biological activity. Now, carbon atoms and hydrogen atoms are the basic building blocks of organic molecules, and fragments of molecules containing only carbon–hydrogen (C—H) single bonds generally have little chemical activity. So, when we want to investigate compounds to identify what contributes to their reactivity a common approach is to design simpler substances by replacing a reactive functional group in a molecule by an unreactive hydrogen atom and observing the result.

One of the compounds that has been tested, phenylethanolamine, **6.4**, is similar to ephedrine in some respects but it is *not* active when taken orally. Phenylethanolamine resembles ephedrine (**6.2**); it contains three fragment groups from ephedrine, but the nitrogen atom of the amine group carries a hydrogen instead of a methyl group.

Other compounds found to have biological activity are phenylethylamine, **6.5**, amphetamine, **6.6**, and methylamphetamine, **6.7**.

Phenylethylamine carries only two of the fragments of ephedrine – the benzene ring, and the amine group (although this does not bear a methyl group) – whereas amphetamine and methylamphetamine contain three of the fragments of ephedrine – the benzene ring and the amine and branching methyl groups.

Of the three, the two amphetamines are by far the more active, with methylamphetamine the most potent.

● What can you deduce from this information about the structural features required for activity?

● Since amphetamine is more active than phenylethylamine it would appear that a branching methyl group is important, and by comparing the activities of methylamphetamine with amphetamine it would appear that the amine nitrogen atom should also bear a methyl group.

Both amphetamine and methylamphetamine have been used to treat asthma; amphetamine was marketed as Benzedrine® and methylamphetamine as Methedrine®, being inhaled as a spray. Unfortunately, like ephedrine, the amphetamines also produce an increase in blood pressure that in extreme cases can lead to heart failure. An equally serious drawback is their ability to act as addictive stimulants when they enter into the brain from the bloodstream.

So, the need for a suitable alternative is apparent, but where to start?

Until recently, the major problem with any approach of this sort, which is based on a lead compound isolated from a natural source, is that an understanding of how it interacts with the molecules of the body is usually unknown. If we knew, even in an elementary way, how ephedrine interacts with biological molecules then the ability to design more efficient drugs would be possible.

## 6.4 Hormones help!

Real progress in the development of a drug to treat the symptoms of asthma came following the discovery of the molecule that the body itself uses to dilate (i.e. to make wider or to cause to expand) the respiratory tract. This molecule is adrenalin, **6.8**.

Adrenalin is secreted into the bloodstream by the adrenal glands that are located above the kidneys in the lower back. It is a natural hormone that acts on distant organs, such as the lung, heart, uterus and gut. Adrenalin brings about its biological effects by binding to receptors on the cell surfaces in each organ.

**6.4** phenylethanolamine

**6.5** phenylethylamine

**6.6** amphetamine

**6.7** methylamphetamine

**6.8** adrenalin

When adrenalin binds to these receptors, it triggers a cascade of reactions inside the cells, and it is this cascade of reactions that causes the biological response. This is represented in Figure 6.6 by the conversion of X into Y. So, if we work out how adrenalin binds to its receptor then we could design a molecule that incorporates these features and which should have a greater biological activity. Easy to say, less easy to carry out in practice!

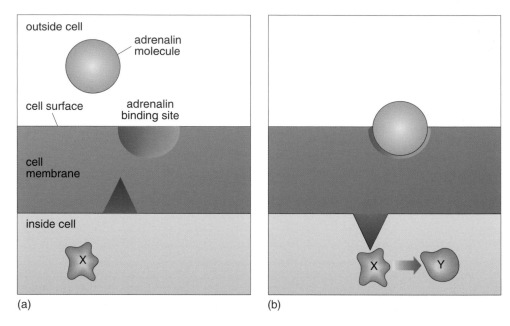

**Figure 6.6**   A representation of how adrenalin brings about its biological action. Adrenalin binds to a receptor (a) and triggers changes within the cell (b).

● Compare the molecular structures of adrenalin, **6.8**, ephedrine, **6.2**, and methylamphetamine, **6.7**, shown again for ease of reference below. What similarities between adrenalin and the other two compounds can you see, and what differences?

**6.8** adrenalin

**6.7** methylamphetamine

**6.2** ephedrine

● Table 6.1 summarises which groups are present in each compound.

**Table 6.1** Comparison of groups in adrenalin, **6.8**, ephedrine, **6.2**, and methylamphetamine, **6.7**.

| Group | adrenalin | ephedrine | methylamphetamine |
|---|---|---|---|
| H–N–CH$_3$ (with H) | ✓ | ✓ | ✓ |
| H, OH, C group | ✓ | ✓ | ✗ |
| HO– / OH aromatic ring group | ✓ | ✗ | ✗ |
| C–CH$_3$, H group | ✗ | ✓ | ✓ |

Not surprisingly, these similarities and differences are precisely the features that can be exploited to generate new, more specific drugs to treat asthma.

It may have crossed your mind to ask the question, 'If adrenalin is the naturally occurring compound that can open up the airways, why not use adrenalin to treat asthma?' You may be able to answer this question yourself from your own experience. It is common usage to talk about 'getting the adrenalin flowing' when we need to carry out a physically or emotionally demanding activity. In such stressful situations, what usually happens to your body physically before you undertake the activity? You usually find that your heart begins to pound and beats faster. Adrenalin is responsible for these effects.

● So, why would the administration of adrenalin be inappropriate to people with asthma?

● As well as affecting the lungs and bronchial tract, adrenalin would also affect the heart.

There are obviously adrenalin receptors on the heart muscle cells as well as on lung cells. Any useful treatment for asthma must centre on a drug that is selective for the lung receptors rather than the heart receptors. Not a simple task to achieve! Of course, this also identifies a probable reason for any side-effects that may arise from drugs derived from adrenalin.

Further reasons, other than a lack of selectivity, for not using adrenalin directly are first, it is inactive when given by mouth, and second, it has only a short duration of action. Its lack of activity when given orally stems from its poor absorption from the intestines into the bloodstream. Its short duration of action arises naturally because enzymes in the body chemically deactivate the compound – this is the body's way of preventing the heart from being in a permanently stressed state!

Despite these drawbacks, adrenalin has one major advantage over methylamphetamine; it is not addictive. This is because it does not enter into the brain from the bloodstream.

● By looking at structures **6.8** and **6.7**, can you work out the reason why adrenalin doesn't enter the brain?

● The blood is a water-rich medium and is therefore polar, whereas the brain is a lipid-rich (fat-rich) medium and is therefore non-polar. The two —OH groups on the benzene ring of adrenalin make it much more soluble in the water-rich environment and much less soluble in the lipid-rich environment. You may recall that this is exactly the opposite requirement to that of the general anaesthetics that you studied in Chapter 5.

However, the same principles of polarity and non-polarity of molecules provide a good clue to successful drug design – to avoid problems relating to addiction it would make sense to include the —OH groups in any new drug for treating the symptoms of asthma, so that they don't enter the brain.

One such compound is isoprenaline, **6.9**. Its structure is almost identical to that of adrenalin, **6.8**, except that the —CH$_3$ (methyl) group bonded to the nitrogen atom has been replaced by the —CH(CH$_3$)$_2$ (isopropyl) group (hence the name, a contraction of isopropyl and adrenalin).

**6.9** isoprenaline

Until the early 1970s, isoprenaline was the drug of choice in the treatment of asthma. The replacement of the methyl group by an isopropyl group made the compound more able than adrenalin to bind to lung receptors. However, isoprenaline does not discriminate between lung receptors and heart receptors; its ability to bind to the heart receptors is the same as its ability to bind to the lung receptors. This lack of selectivity between heart and lung receptors not surprisingly gives rise to some unpleasant side-effects, such as palpitations or uneven beating of the heart. Another disadvantage of isoprenaline is that, like adrenalin, it has a short duration of activity because the enzymes that deactivate adrenalin also deactivate isoprenaline. So, there's a need to understand both how adrenalin binds to its receptor – by identifying which molecular features are needed for binding – and how it is inactivated.

● How might you identify which of the functional groups in adrenalin are needed for biological activity?

● One possibility would be to design and test other compounds in which one of the groups had been replaced by a hydrogen atom.

**Question 6.1**

Use this strategy to draw the structures of two compounds based on the structure of adrenalin that would test the role of the two —OH groups attached to the benzene ring. ◀

We can then ask ourselves 'Are the —OH groups themselves necessary for effective hydrogen bonding, or can we replace them by some other similar groups?' There are several ways of trying to answer this question. First we could replace either or both of the —OH groups with some other group, for example an amine group —$NH_2$, given the similar electronegativity of the O and N atoms that we discussed in Section 3.2.

Alternatively, we could choose to investigate whether or not the —OH groups have to be attached directly to the benzene ring. We can do that by replacing the —OH group with —$CH_2OH$, effectively by inserting a —$CH_2$— fragment as a spacer group between the ring and the —OH as in **6.10**. How chemists bring about this change is beyond the scope of our course. In the same way as H atoms are often used to replace a group within a molecule, —$CH_2$— groups are often used in this way so that the distances between groups that are thought to be biologically important can be altered and investigated. The functional group is unchanged, the hydrocarbon chain itself is unreactive, so only the distance is changed.

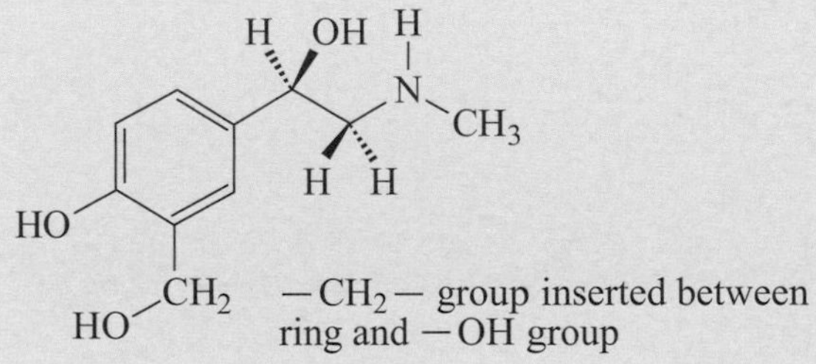

—$CH_2$— group inserted between ring and —OH group

**6.10**

By varying both of the ring —OH groups in these ways, it was found that one is absolutely essential to biological activity, whereas the other can be varied to —$CH_2OH$ or —$CH_2CH_2OH$ but not to —$CH_2CH_2CH_2OH$ (Figure 6.7). Obviously this second —OH group is necessary, but its distance from the ring can be varied within a limited range.

As it turns out, changing the —OH group to —$CH_2OH$ has another profoundly beneficial effect on the biological activity of the molecule – the molecule becomes resistant to deactivation by enzymes, which means that the drug has a much longer duration of action (Box 6.1).

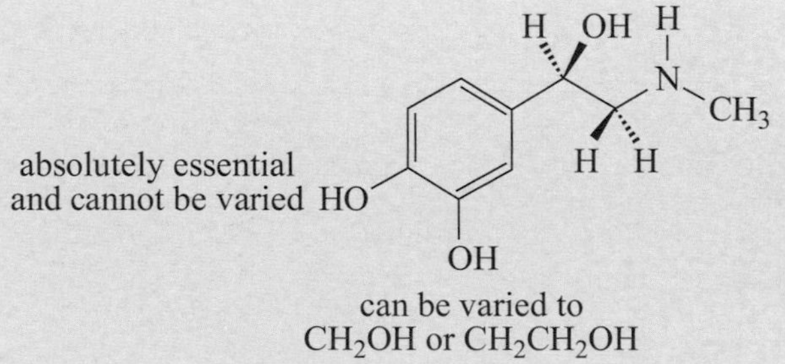

absolutely essential and cannot be varied

can be varied to $CH_2OH$ or $CH_2CH_2OH$

**Figure 6.7** The essential and variable —OH groups on the benzene ring in adrenalin.

### Box 6.1  *Deactivation of adrenalin*

Although several biological processes terminate the action of adrenalin-like compounds, one of the enzymes does so because it converts one of the ring —OH groups in the molecule into an —$OCH_3$ group. Figure 6.8a shows this reaction using simple skeletal structures for the molecules that are involved.

The presence of the —$OCH_3$ apparently blocks the ability of the molecule to bind to the adrenalin receptor. Since enzymes catalyse this reaction it is very specific for the —OH group shown. Neither of the other two —OH groups is affected, and when the —OH that is converted is changed to a —$CH_2OH$ group it too is unaffected by the enzyme and this compound is thus not susceptible to deactivation (Figure 6.8b).

**Figure 6.8**    (a) Deactivation of adrenalin by enzymes. Note how this style of representation of adrenalin differs from that in Figure 6.7. (b) Replacing —OH by —$CH_2OH$ prevents deactivation by enzymes.

## 6.5   Getting together

We can now begin to build up a basic idea of what is required for a molecule to bind to the adrenalin receptor. First, all of the molecules we have been considering contain an aromatic (benzene) ring. Second, they all contain an amine group. So, as a very minimum, these two groups seem to be essential and it seems likely that each has an area of the receptor that will recognise it and bind to it (Figure 6.9a). But this picture can be modified, because we know that compounds with —OH groups attached to the benzene ring are more active molecules than ephedrine-like molecules that lack these groups (Figure 6.9b).

We might consider whether or not the —OH group on the carbon chain is needed. After all, both adrenalin and ephedrine contain the group, but amphetamine doesn't.

● How might you try to determine if this —OH group is necessary for binding?

● By making and testing a molecule such as **6.11** in which the —OH has been replaced by a hydrogen atom.

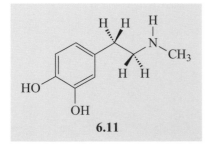

**6.11**

Actually, we already know that an —OH in this position is not essential for biological activity because compounds such as amphetamine are active. It does contribute to the selectivity of the compound though. When compounds similar to adrenalin but with the —H and —OH groups interchanged are tested, they are found to be more than 50 times less active than the adrenalin itself (Figure 6.10).

You might remember that this is the same kind of result that is seen with ephedrine and pseudoephedrine. Ephedrine, **6.2**, has the —H and —OH groups arranged as in adrenalin and it has anti-asthmatic activity; pseudoephedrine, **6.3**, has the —H and —OH groups interchanged as shown in Figure 6.10, and it has activity on the heart but no anti-asthmatic activity.

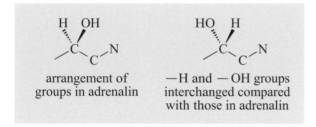

**Figure 6.10** Interchange of —H and —OH groups in adrenalin leading to reduced activity.

Clearly, the spatial position of this particular —OH group is important too. So, our picture of the receptor should be modified still further to accommodate binding to the —OH group (Figure 6.9c). This sketch-like picture of the receptor is a very basic representation of the interactions that are involved in three dimensions when a molecule binds to it, but we can begin to see that the more binding sites there are the more specific are the structures of the molecules that bind.

In Section 3.2 we discussed the different forces that are involved in these binding sites.

● What are the names of the three types of binding force that can be involved in the intermolecular attraction of drugs with enzymes or receptors?

● Hydrogen bonding, London forces and ionic attractions.

● Look at each of the binding sites in the adrenalin receptor depicted in Figure 6.9c and decide which forces would be involved in each of them.

● The —OH groups would bind via hydrogen bonding, the aromatic binding site would involve London forces between the benzene ring and the receptor, and finally the amine binding site as depicted in the figure would rely on hydrogen bonding. However, if the amine group was positively charged, as in Reaction 4.3, then there would be the possibility of an ionic attraction with this binding site.

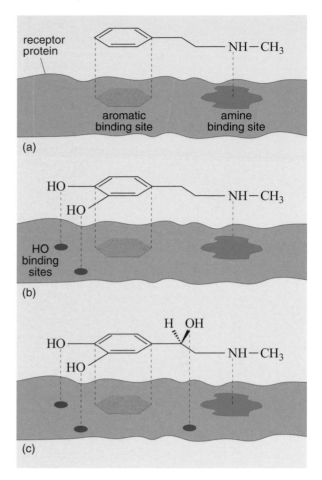

**Figure 6.9** A representation of the adrenalin receptor in a protein: (a) taking account of the aromatic and amine groups; (b) including the —OH groups attached to the ring; (c) including the —OH group of the carbon chain.

How many binding sites do we need to get selective binding to a particular molecule? To answer this question, try Activity 6.2.

### Activity 6.2

Make the two models of the stereoisomers (mirror image molecules) shown in Figure 6.11 and orientate them as shown in the figure.

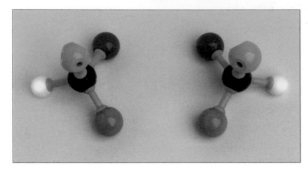

**Figure 6.12**   Representation (model) of a receptor with two binding sites 6.5 cm apart (centre to centre) on the scale of the molecular model kit.

**Figure 6.11**   Models of the two stereoisomers for use in Activity 6.2.

Suppose a receptor has two binding sites, separated by a distance 6.5 cm apart that can be represented by Figure 6.12. Now, let's assume site 1 in Figure 6.12 binds to a blue centre and site 2 binds to a red centre.

● Use your models to see if you can arrange for the blue and red centres of each of the molecules to bind to their appropriate sites in the receptor. What do you find?

● You should find that both can be easily arranged so that the blue group can bind to site 1 and the red group to site 2.

So our finding is that a two-site receptor is not sufficient to distinguish between these different molecules.

What happens if we add another binding site, so the receptor now has three sites? Let's assume the third site recognises green groups (Figure 6.13).

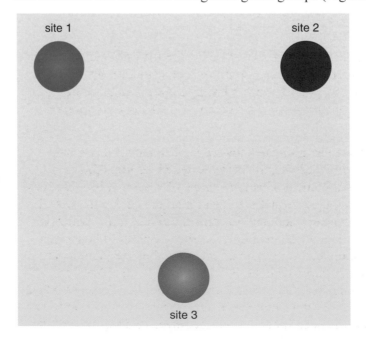

**Figure 6.13**   A model of a three-site receptor.

● Now try to arrange your models so that they bind to the receptor at all three sites. What do you find?

● You should find that only one of the models will fit all three sites at the same time; the other can only fit two of the sites.

Two conclusions that we can draw from this simple activity are: (i) a receptor requires at least three binding sites in order to differentiate between different molecules that are mirror images of each other (stereoisomers) and (ii) the more binding sites there are, the more selective the binding can be.

The amphetamines contain a benzene ring and an amine group that can bind to two of the sites on the adrenalin receptor and produce a clear effect. So, even with several binding sites, a receptor is not guaranteed to have a specific response to only one or even a limited range of compounds. To obtain selective drug action, what is needed is a receptor with several binding sites (at least three, preferably more), and a drug with several groups (at least three, preferably more) which will bind to these receptor sites, as shown in Figure 6.9c. Now it's becoming clear why developing a drug without side-effects is so very difficult to achieve!

## 6.6 Asthma drugs

Combining the information obtained from these studies with the observation that isoprenaline is more selective than adrenalin enabled chemists to design compound **6.12**, salbutamol.

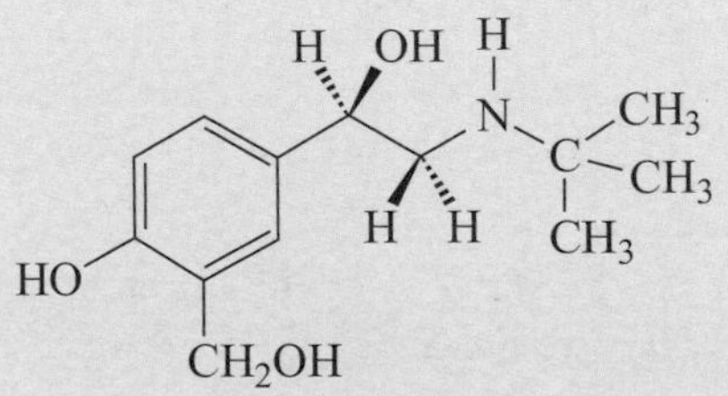

**6.12** salbutamol

This compound contains all the features we've discovered, except that it has a tertiary butyl group (Figure 6.14) attached to the nitrogen atom rather than an isopropyl group. These hydrocarbon groups are similar, but for this set of compounds the tertiary butyl group gives the compound a longer duration of biological activity.

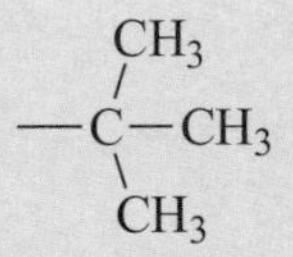

People with asthma will have an intimate knowledge of salbutamol – it is the active ingredient in Ventolin®. Salbutamol has superseded isoprenaline as the compound of choice in the treatment of asthma, largely because of its selectivity of action. Isoprenaline has roughly equal activity as a dilator of the airways of the respiratory tract and as a heart stimulant. In contrast, salbutamol – which is just as good a bronchial dilator as isoprenaline – is about 200 times better as a dilator than as a heart stimulant. So, the side-effects of taking salbutamol have been reduced drastically compared with the first lead compound ephedrine, which is both addictive and a heart stimulant, and adrenalin, which is also a heart stimulant. Even so, research to find a more effective drug continued on at least two fronts; first there was the need for an even more selective drug, and second

tertiary butyl group

**Figure 6.14** Tertiary butyl group.

there was the more pressing need to discover a drug that would be able to afford protection against an asthma attack for periods longer than the 4 hours that salbutamol provides. Researchers eventually hit the ideal candidate by replacing the large tertiary butyl group of salbutamol with the highly non-polar group $-(CH_2)_6O(CH_2)_4C_6H_5$, which enabled the drug salmetrol **6.13** to dissolve readily in cell membranes and thus be longer acting. This was in addition to retaining the three $-OH$ groups present in salbutamol that provide a degree of water solubility and help to prevent the drug crossing the blood–brain barrier.

Salmetrol, marketed as Serevent®, has altered the treatment of asthma, giving patients 24-hour protection by taking it just twice a day. It has not completely replaced salbutamol because salbutamol is still used for immediate relief of wheezing or shortness of breath.

**6.13**  salmetrol

## 6.7    Reflection

Our story of the discovery of salbutamol and salmetrol has developed a long way from the original 'lead' provided by *ma huang*. It is worth reviewing the process involved.

*   A naturally occurring material, in this case a plant, is observed to have desirable biological activity.

*   The constituent responsible for the biological activity is isolated from the material and its chemical structure identified.

*   The structure of the active constituent is used as a starting point for the development of molecules with similar structures in an attempt to improve on the biological activity of the naturally occurring compound.

*   An understanding of the molecular features required for the interactions with biological molecules that give rise to physiological activity is built up.

*   The important molecular interactions are used to design further compounds that are expected to be both more potent and more selective.

Now try the following questions to test your understanding of the chemical principles you have been learning about. It is worth working carefully through these questions and if anything is unclear go back to the text and re-read it.

**Question 6.2**

Study the structure of molecules **6.14**, **6.15** and **6.16**. Which of them would you predict will bind to both the aromatic binding site and the amine binding site of the adrenalin receptor (Figure 6.9)?   ◀

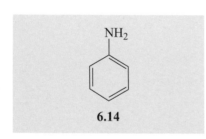

**6.14**

**6.15**

**6.16**

**Question 6.3**

A receptor has been identified that is capable of binding to an $-NH_2$ group and an $-SH$ group. On the scale of the molecular model kit these binding sites are 12.5 cm apart (Figure 6.15).

**Figure 6.15** Representation of a two-site receptor for $-SH$ and $-NH_2$ groups, 12.5 cm apart.

(a) Use your model kit to design the backbone of the simplest molecule that would be capable of binding to the receptor in Figure 6.15. (*Hint*: think what other atoms might be needed to separate the two groups by the correct distance.)

(b) Would either of the compounds **6.17** and **6.18** bind to this receptor? ◄

**Question 6.4**

You suspect that the oxygen atom of compound **6.19** is important for it to bind to a receptor. Suggest two compounds that you would use to test whether or not your suspicions were correct. ◄

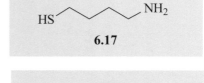

6.17

6.18

# 6.8 Summary of Chapter 6

In this chapter you've learnt that:

- Ephedrine can be isolated from the Chinese herbal remedy *ma huang*.

- Ephedrine has anti-asthmatic properties as well as heart stimulant properties.

- Using the molecular structure of ephedrine as a lead, the amphetamines were developed; these have undesirable side-effects – they increase blood pressure and are addictive.

- Ephedrine and amphetamine exert their anti-asthmatic and heart stimulating activities by binding to the adrenalin receptor on the lungs and heart.

- Compounds based on the structure of adrenalin are non-addictive because the presence of two $-OH$ groups on the benzene ring means that the compounds are polar and therefore unable to cross the blood–brain barrier.

- By modifying the structure of adrenalin, first isoprenaline and subsequently salbutamol and salmetrol were developed as anti-asthmatic drugs. Salbutamol is much more selective for the lung adrenalin receptors than the heart receptors. So is salmetrol and it has the added advantage of a drug that has a longer lasting action.

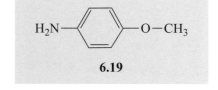

6.19

You have also discovered:

- That to test whether a group within a molecule is important to biological activity it is possible to design (and subsequently test) a similar molecule in which either the group has been replaced by a hydrogen atom or has been interchanged with a similar group, e.g. $-OH$ for $-NH_2$.

- That to test whether the distance between particular groups is important to biological activity, new compounds can be designed in which spacer $-CH_2-$ groups are inserted between the groups under study.

- How to use molecular models to determine whether or not a particular compound will fit to a representation of a receptor, as well as to design molecules that can fit to particular binding sites in a receptor.

# Captopril – a landmark in drug design

**7**

So far, you have seen that the development of new drugs relies heavily on having a lead compound. More often than not the lead compound is a naturally occurring compound, e.g. cocaine, which has been isolated from a plant. Alternatively, synthetic compounds are found to have unexpected biological activity, providing novel types of compound to study; the sulfonamides that you will meet in Chapter 8 are an example. Once the structure of the lead compound is known, similar compounds (analogues) can be made and tested so that the molecular features that give rise to the biological activity can be optimised. You might reasonably guess that captopril, a drug used to treat high blood pressure, was discovered in this way. In fact, a somewhat different approach was followed, as you will see in this chapter – not that there is a lack of traditional remedies for high blood pressure. The 17th century herbalist Nicholas Culpeper knew about many of these (Figure 7.1). He wrote:

*Lime tree* … the flowers are excellent for apoplexy and palpitation of the heart …

*Hawthorn* … the seeds in the berries beaten to a powder being drunk in wine, are good against the stone and dropsy [dropsy is a heart condition which involves excess fluid retention].

*Dandelion* … it openeth the passages of the urine both in young and old …… it helpeth also to procure rest and sleep …

**Figure 7.1** (a) Lime trees, (b) hawthorn and (c) dandelions – plants that have the ability to relieve high blood pressure.

(a)

(b)

(c)

## 7.1    Blood pressure

Modern research has shown that both lime flowers and hawthorn berries contain a group of chemical compounds called flavonoids, and it is these compounds that reduce blood pressure. These flavonoids are also present in dark chocolate and red wine. However, this is where the development of captopril differs from the traditional story of drug development, as captopril is not a flavonoid, neither was it developed from them.

Instead, captopril was designed using what has become known as the rational approach to drug design. For this approach, there has to be a good, though not necessarily complete, understanding of the biological system that gives rise to a particular effect. Then the rational approach is to design a compound that can interact with the system in a desirable way. You will see how this was achieved for captopril.

One mechanism by which human blood pressure is controlled is called the renin–angiotensin system. In this system angiotensinogen, a protein, is cleaved (split) by the enzyme renin to form angiotensin I. This in turn is cleaved to form angiotensin II by an enzyme found in the lungs and blood vessels called angiotensin converting enzyme, or ACE for short (Reaction 7.1).

$$\text{angiotensinogen} \xrightarrow{\text{renin}} \text{angiotensin I} \xrightarrow{\text{ACE}} \text{angiotensin II} \qquad (7.1)$$

Angiotensin II is the chemical in this system that has all the biological activity. First, it constricts blood vessels and that causes blood pressure to increase – it takes more pressure to pump a fluid through narrow tubes than wide ones. Second, it controls the release of a hormone, aldosterone, which is a chemical messenger that regulates the excretion of potassium ions, $K^+$, and the retention of water and sodium ions, $Na^+$. Retention of water and sodium ions also increases blood pressure.

Unlike angiotensin II, angiotensin I has no biological activity of its own, making ACE a key enzyme in blood pressure regulation. In fact, more so than the above picture might indicate, since ACE also converts another biological compound, bradykinin – which reduces blood pressure by dilating blood vessels – into biologically inactive compounds. So, as well as increasing blood pressure in its own right, ACE also prevents bradykinin from lowering blood pressure.

## 7.2    Possible treatment

This understanding gives us the beginning of a molecular approach to treating high blood pressure: if we can reduce the amount of angiotensin II being produced, then blood pressure should fall. But how is it possible to achieve that? Well, the enzyme ACE binds to angiotensin I and converts it into the product, angiotensin II. So, if it is possible to block the active site of ACE so that angiotensin I cannot bind to the enzyme, then no angiotensin II can be produced. This ought to be possible if a drug is administered that the enzyme binds to in preference. In essence, the drug and angiotensin I *compete* for the enzyme. So the problem for the chemist boils down to one of designing a molecule that has the right features that allow it to bind to the enzyme in preference to angiotensin I. The starting point here is not the molecular structure of a known drug, but the nature of the biological, enzyme-catalysed process. It is this understanding of the biology that drives the design of an appropriate drug by the rational approach. Let's take a closer look at this process.

Angiotensin I is a peptide (a small protein molecule) formed by 10 amino acids linked together in a linear chain. Using the three-letter abbreviation system for amino acids that was introduced in Section 3.1.1, the structure of angiotensin I can be written as shown in Figure 7.2a where the amino acid aspartic acid (Asp) is linked to arginine (Arg), which is linked to valine (Val) and so on until histidine (His) and leucine (Leu). The enzyme ACE binds to angiotensin I and specifically cleaves two amino acids, histidine and leucine (His, Leu), from the carboxylic acid end of the peptide (Figure 7.2b) to form angiotensin II, which is made up of eight amino acids.

When an enzyme cleaves a peptide or protein, the amide (peptide) bond linking two amino acid groups together is broken (Figure 7.3).

Now we know that ACE cleaves two amino acids from the end of the peptide. At the outset of research in the mid-1960s, it was also known that each ACE molecule contains one zinc ion, $Zn^{2+}$, which is a zinc atom that has lost two electrons. What is needed, then, is a molecule that mimics one end of angiotensin I, and which will be bound in preference to angiotensin I by ACE.

Before we can explore what such a molecule looks like, we need first to gain a better understanding of exactly what the enzyme does.

## 7.3 How does ACE work?

Figure 7.2 is the starting point for understanding how ACE works. Given the fact that two specific amino acids (His, Leu) are cleaved from angiotensin I let's try to build up a useful pictorial model of which functional groups are involved in the active site of the enzyme.

A first, and reasonable, supposition is that the carboxylic acid group at the end of the peptide chain is essential, and binds to the enzyme.

● Why is this a reasonable supposition?

● Because it is from the carboxylic acid end of angiotensin I that the two amino acids are cleaved (Figure 7.2b).

Based on the way other enzymes are known to work, it is also reasonable to assume that the $Zn^{2+}$ ion is involved; in fact it activates the amide bond to be broken. The zinc ion is positively

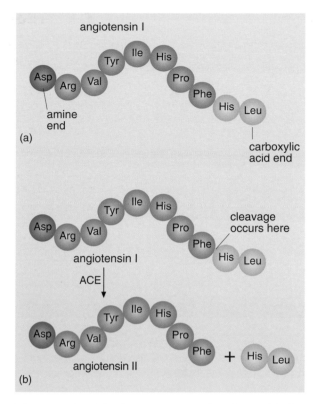

**Figure 7.2** (a) The sequence of amino acids in angiotensin I. (b) The formation of angiotensin II from angiotensin I by the action of ACE.

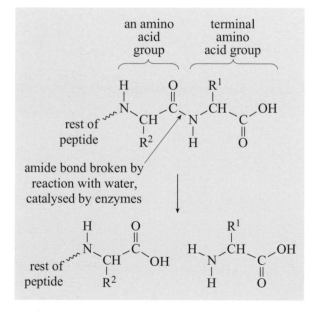

**Figure 7.3** Breaking an amide (peptide) bond by an enzyme.

charged and it can attract the O in the C=O group of the amide bond that is to be cleaved because the oxygen has a $\delta-$ charge on it (while the carbon has a $\delta+$ charge). This attraction is referred to as an ion-dipole attraction. This dipole arises because the oxygen atom is more electronegative than carbon. Return to Section 3.2.2 if you need to review dipole attractions. With ACE, the *two* amino acids at the end are removed. So, in ACE the $Zn^{2+}$ binding site must lie a specific distance from the binding site for the carboxylic acid group.

If these assumptions are correct then we can begin to build up a schematic model, shown in Figure 7.4, of how the angiotensin I interacts with ACE. Don't forget that in reality these interactions take place in three dimensions.

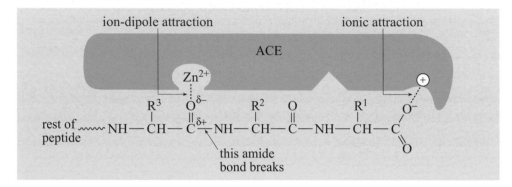

**Figure 7.4**   The beginnings of a schematic representation (model) for the active site in ACE with a partial structure for angiotensin I for simplicity.

So, we might predict that a first requirement for any drug to treat high blood pressure will be that it contains a carboxylic acid functional group separated from another group capable of binding to a $Zn^{2+}$ ion. The distance between these two groups ought to be similar to that in the peptide angiotensin I, i.e. about six bonds (Figure 7.5).

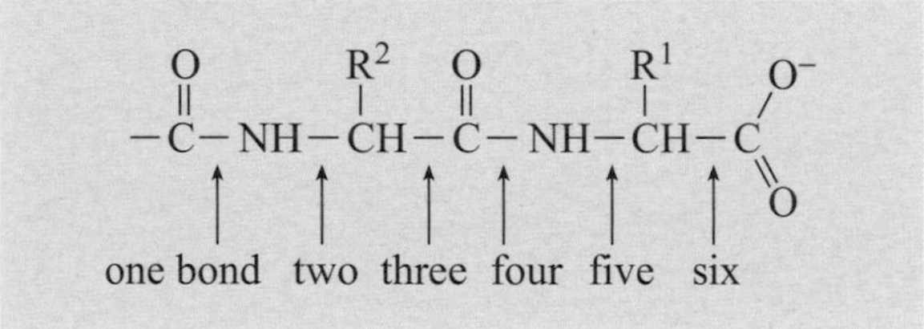

**Figure 7.5**   Bond counting in part of angiotensin I.

Of course, the drug itself ought not to be a compound that ACE reacts with, otherwise the drug too would be broken down just like angiotensin I and would therefore be unable to carry out its function of blocking the enzyme.

●   Remembering the chemistry that ACE carries out, what type of bond must a potential drug molecule *not* contain?

●   It must not contain an amide that could bind to $Zn^{2+}$ in ACE, otherwise it will be cleaved and the drug destroyed (see Figure 7.4).

The model for ACE arrived at so far does not take any account of the type of interactions that occur with the groups $R^1$ and $R^2$ in a potential drug . Nor for that matter have we identified what the groups $R^1$ and $R^2$ might be. Figure 7.4 suggests that these could be any groups, but this is highly unlikely. Most enzymes will bind to a preferred type of group at each position. The problem facing us is the same as that facing the original researchers: 'Which groups to choose?' Without any further information we would have to try the 'suck-it-and-see' approach of developing a drug from a lead compound: trying one group, then another, and another and so on until the best one was found. This would be very hit-and-miss, as well as time consuming. Fortunately, a further piece of information was available in this chemical jigsaw. A series of peptides isolated from the venom of various species of viper were found to block the formation of angiotensin II by ACE. They were all powerful 'ACE inhibitors', i.e. they block the enzyme, and each of them had the amino acid proline **7.1** as the terminal amino acid.

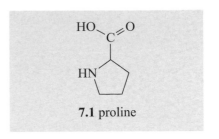

**7.1 proline**

Significantly, these peptides are also able to reduce blood pressure, as we would predict if they compete with angiotensin I for ACE. The compounds, therefore, provide us with the confidence that the original hypothesis was correct and also tell us that the schematic model of ACE needs refining to incorporate the binding of a terminal proline. This is shown in Figure 7.6.

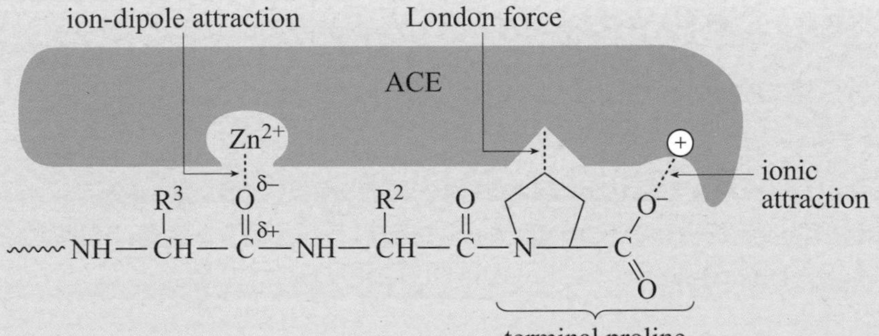

**Figure 7.6** A modified schematic model for a molecule to bind and block ACE.

- Jot down all the requirements identified so far that would need to be incorporated into the structure of an ACE inhibitor drug.

- The drug should have:
  - a carboxylic acid, that exists as a carboxylate anion ($-COO^-$) at one end, preferably as part of a proline group;
  - a C=O group that can bind to a $Zn^{2+}$ ion;
  - the two groups should be separated by about six bonds;
  - the C=O group that binds to the $Zn^{2+}$ ion should not be part of an amide group.

If we start putting these requirements together we get a partial molecular structure for the drug that looks something like Figure 7.7.

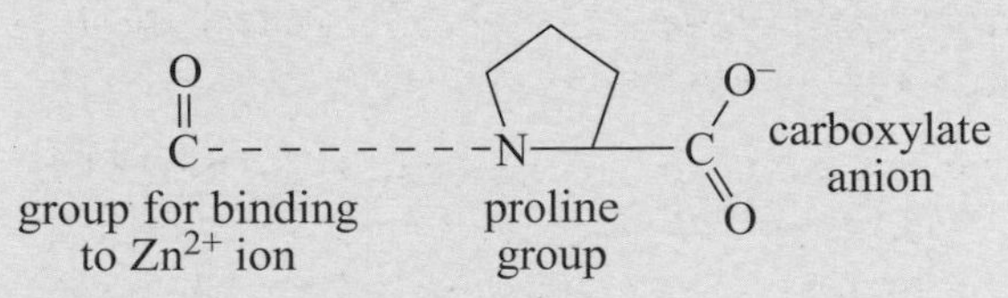

**Figure 7.7** A partial molecular structure for an ACE inhibitor.

We now have to fill in the missing fragments of the structure represented by the dashed line in Figure 7.7.

● How many extra bonds are needed to meet the requirement that there should be six between the carboxylic acid group and the $Zn^{2+}$ binding group?

● The proline group contains two of the bonds and six are required, so another four bonds are needed to get the correct spacing.

● Which group can be used to act as a spacer in a molecule? How many will be needed to get the correct spacing for our ACE drug?

● The $-CH_2-$ group is often used as a spacer because it is chemically very unreactive – it thus provides structure not function. Three such groups will be needed to get the correct spacing.

Our design for an ACE inhibitor drug now looks like Figure 7.8. Notice how inserting three $-CH_2-$ spacer groups involves four additional bonds. Using $-CH_2-$ groups in this way has allowed us to replace the C—N bond in the amide at the $Zn^{2+}$ binding end of the molecule with a C—C bond. This is just what is needed, because such C—C bonds are resistant to cleavage.

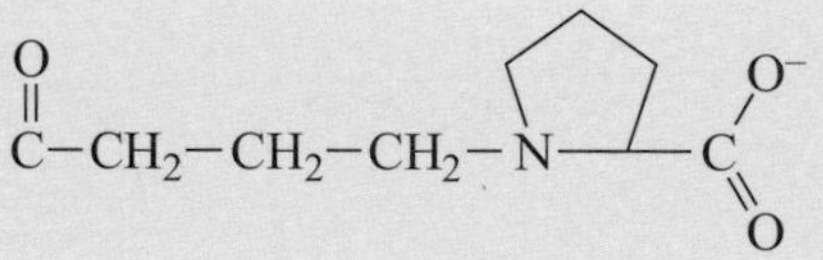

**Figure 7.8** ACE inhibitor design – spacer groups included.

● In what way is the structure of the molecule still incomplete?

● The carbon atom at the $Zn^{2+}$ binding end is only involved in three bonds, whereas it requires four to ensure it has the correct valency.

As well as binding to the C=O group in the amide via the dipole interaction that we have discussed, $Zn^{2+}$ will also bind to carboxylic acids since this functional group exists as $-COO^-$ in the enzyme and there is then an ionic attraction between the groups. This information should prompt us to suggest that the $Zn^{2+}$ binding group in our proposed drug could be a carboxylic acid. So our suggested drug design is now shown in Figure 7.9.

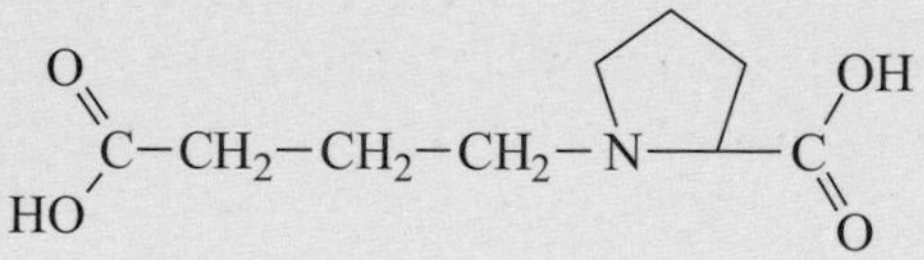

**Figure 7.9** ACE inhibitor design – carboxylic acids at both ends.

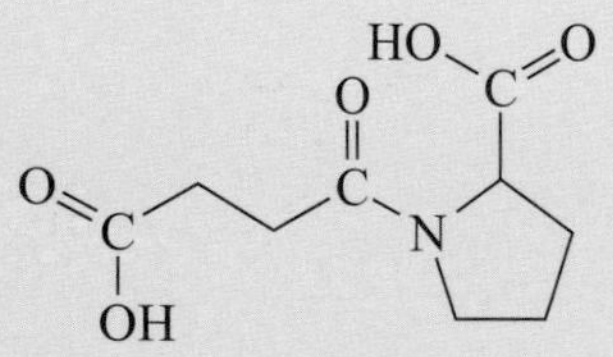

This is a perfectly reasonable molecule to try to make and test, but in practice, succinylproline (pronounced 'suck-sin-isle-pro-leen') **7.2**, is the compound of choice.

**7.2 succinylproline**

● Compare **7.2** with Figure 7.9 and state any differences.

● The only difference between the two is that in succinylproline the carbon atom of the spacer group directly bonded to the nitrogen atom is part of a C=O system rather than $-CH_2-$. There are two reasons for this. The first is that in the normal substrate (angiotensin I) for the enzyme this carbon atom is part of a C=O group. So succinylproline resembles the normal substrates better than the compound we designed. The second is to do with the way the compounds are made in the laboratory. It turns out that it is easier to make the compound with a C=O rather than a $-CH_2-$ next to the proline.

Succinylproline does indeed compete with angiotensin I for ACE, but its activity as an inhibitor of ACE doesn't come close to that of the peptides isolated from snake venom. So we need to modify the structure of succinylproline in some way to increase activity. One possibility is to assume that there is a site on the enzyme that interacts with the group $R^2$ of the substrate (Figure 7.10). We would then need to position a similar group in succinylproline. The simplest group to add is methyl, $-CH_3$, because it is small and has no functional group. If we make this change then the compound we obtain is methyl-substituted succinylproline, **7.3**.

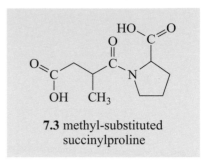

**7.3** methyl-substituted succinylproline

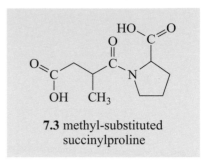

**Figure 7.10** A further modified model for the active site in ACE, showing the binding interactions.

● What do you notice about the groups around the carbon atom which carries the methyl group in **7.3**? What is special about this carbon atom?

● The groups are all different, ($-CH_3$, $-CH_2-$, C=O, and $-H$) so the carbon atom is chiral (Section 6.2).

As you saw in the last chapter, the fact that we have a chiral carbon means there are two stereoisomers with this structure. The data in Table 7.1 show that one of these stereoisomers is ten times more active than methyl-substituted succinylproline, **7.3** – itself a mixture of both stereoisomers – whereas the other is less than half as active as methyl-substituted succinylproline. These results tell us that there must indeed be a site on the enzyme that interacts with the methyl group and that it is specifically oriented in space – don't forget, the model (Figure 7.10) is a two-dimensional representation of what occurs in three dimensions. Yet again you can see how the activity of a potential drug depends on its ability to fit precisely into the enzyme's active site. Small changes to the structure result in subtle alterations in shape that in turn can lead to large changes in the activity of a drug.

The results so far are promising, but we still need to build something extra into the molecules that will make them interact with the enzyme more strongly. One approach might be to vary the methyl group in methyl-substituted succinylproline, **7.3**, with other groups until we have maximised the strength of the interaction with the enzyme. Another is to optimise the interaction with the zinc ion. In angiotensin I this interaction involves an amide group but in our model drug compounds it involves a carboxylic acid.

We might question whether these are the groups that form the strongest interactions with $Zn^{2+}$ ions.

**Table 7.1** Relative activities of some compounds that bind to ACE.

| Compound | Relative activity |
|---|---|
| | 1 |
| | 10 |
| | 0.4 |

**Table 7.2** Binding strengths of some simple compounds to bind $Zn^{2+}$.

| Compound | Relative binding strength |
|---|---|
| $H_2N-CH_2-CH_2-NH_2$ | 800 |
| $H_2N-CH_2-CH_2-OH$ | 1 |
| $H_2N-CH_2-CH_2-SH$ | 4 000 000 |
| $H_2N-CH_2-C(=O)-OH$ | 200 |

**7.4** captopril

● Take a look at Table 7.2, which contains the relative binding strengths of four simple organic compounds for $Zn^{2+}$ ions. From these values which group do you think binds best to $Zn^{2+}$?

● From the relative sizes of the binding strength it is quite clear that the sulfur-containing compound binds much more strongly to $Zn^{2+}$ than compounds containing the other groups, by a factor of up to 4 million.

The data in Table 7.2 strongly suggest that we should modify our drug molecule **7.3** by removing the carboxylic acid group, —COOH, and replacing it with —SH, a thiol (pronounced 'thigh-ol') group, if binding to $Zn^{2+}$ is important. This binding is an ionic attraction between $Zn^{2+}$ and —S⁻ as the —SH group loses an $H^+$ in the enzyme active site. If we do that, combined with all our deductions so far, the compound we get is **7.4**. When this compound is tested for its ability to compete with angiotensin I for ACE it is found to be much more active than the succinylproline compound. Binding to the $Zn^{2+}$ site of the enzyme is quite clearly important. Compound **7.4** is known as captopril and it is an effective treatment for both high blood pressure and heart failure. If we were to include captopril in Table 7.1 its relative activity would be 25 000.

Captopril, marketed as Capoten®, came onto the drugs market in 1980 and was the first compound designed to compete with angiotensin I for ACE. Since then, other compounds have appeared, each developed by continuing the logical design arguments (rational approach) used to design captopril. The more the nature of the enzyme-binding site is established, the more the structure of the drug can be refined. On its own, captopril is able to reduce the blood pressure in around 50% of people with high blood pressure. However, in combination with a diuretic – that is, a drug that aids the flow of urine and therefore diminishes water retention – this figure rises to 90%. So using the two medicines in combination brings about a significant improvement in the treatment. Hence our story comes full circle, as this is very reminiscent of the suggested treatment of high blood pressure using herbal medicines with which we started this chapter.

In its own way, the development of captopril has proved to be a landmark in the chemistry of drug design. Whereas in earlier times drugs were developed solely from lead compounds discovered to have biological activity, captopril was developed from the known function of the target enzyme and designed to interact with the important features of the enzyme. By building up a simple model of the important enzyme sites, it has been possible to design a drug that is able to compete with angiotensin I for those sites, and by so doing to prevent angiotensin I being converted into angiotensin II.

**Question 7.1**

If snake venom provides several peptides that are powerful inhibitors of ACE why not use these, taken orally, as drugs to treat high blood pressure? *(Hint: what happens to peptides when eaten?)* ◀

**Question 7.2**

Look back to Figures 7.4, 7.6 and 7.10, in which the carboxylic acid end of the molecule is shown bound to ACE. What type of group would need to be present in ACE in order to give this attraction? ◀

**Question 7.3**

Why do you think captopril is used in the treatment of heart failure? ◀

## 7.4 Summary of Chapter 7

In this chapter you have learnt that:

- Captopril is a drug that is used to reduce high blood pressure; it works by inhibiting (blocking) the angiotensin converting enzyme (ACE).

- Captopril was developed by carefully and logically building up a model of the molecular requirements that are needed for it to bind to the enzyme active site, rather than simply modifying the molecular structure of a lead compound.

## 7.5 Reflection

A useful way of thinking back over any course is to look for 'overarching themes' which link together otherwise apparently unconnected topics, by looking at features that turn out to be common. If you look back over your study of drugs that are designed to achieve some very different outcomes you should be able to identify the 'overarching theme' of binding to receptors. Before you move on, make sure you are familiar with the binding attractions that are turning out to be common to the action of almost all drugs.

# 8 War on bad bacteria – antiseptics, disinfectants and antibiotics

So, naturalists observe, a flea
Hath smaller fleas that on him prey;
And these have smaller still to bite 'em;
And so proceed ad infinitum.

Jonathan Swift (1667–1745)

It was one of Swift's contemporaries, the Dutch microscopist Anton van Leeuwenhoek (1632–1723) who first reported, in 1683, the observation of what could only have been bacteria (single-celled organisms). The observations were made at the limit of what could be seen with his microscopes that could magnify up to around 300 times and, as far as is known, about 100 years passed before anyone else observed them again. A further 50 years were to pass before it started to be recognised that a major cause of illness arose from infections that could easily be avoided by taking suitable hygiene precautions. It was found in 1842, by Holmes in the USA, and in 1847, by Semmelweis in Vienna, that the often-fatal condition of childbirth fever could be almost completely avoided if health care workers disinfected their hands before working with patients. In 1865 Louis Pasteur suggested that decay of tissue was caused by microscopic living organisms (bacteria) in the air and Joseph Lister was quick to spot the connection with infection of wounds. He started using a solution of phenol to cleanse wounds and was able to report the defeat of postoperative infection in his hospital. Phenol will be important in this chapter, so if you cannot remember its structural formula, look back to **2.3** in Section 2.4.1, where its structure is described in detail. Bacteria are just one type of microbe (microorganism) capable of causing disease. Others include viruses, to be discussed in Chapter 9, and fungi (moulds), which we will not cover in this course.

## 8.1 Good and harmful bacteria

Although this chapter is concerned with controlling harmful bacteria it would be wrong not to make at least a mention of 'good' bacteria. Without bacteria, life on Earth would not exist in the form that we know it; almost certainly it would not exist at all. There is considerable evidence that bacteria were the earliest life forms that evolved on Earth and it is the fossil remains of these single-celled organisms that are looked for by expeditions to other planets or their moons in order to try to establish whether life forms may once have existed there.

Good bacteria exist extensively on and within a healthy human body; in fact there are usually many more bacterial cells present than there are of our own cells! These good bacteria are involved in many essential bodily processes. For example, when these bacteria are missing, perhaps because a course of antibiotics has destroyed them along with the harmful bacteria, our digestive system does not function as well as it should, until the colony of good bacteria can re-establish itself. Nowadays, it has become fashionable to maintain a healthy complement of so-called 'probiotic' bacteria in our gut by choice of diet, e.g. by eating yoghurts containing lactobacilli (Figure 8.1).

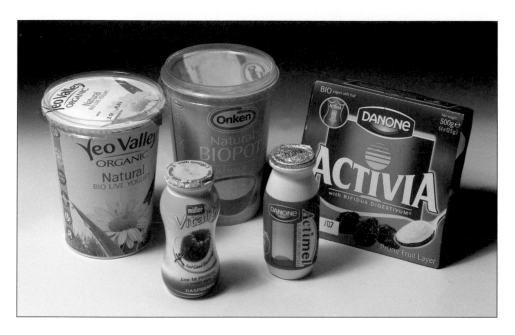

**Figure 8.1** Some dietary foods that are said to contain useful bacteria.

Harmful, or pathogenic (disease-producing), bacteria interfere with the normal processes going on in a healthy body. There are many ways in which they can do this; for example, they may invade our cells and destroy them, using the contents for food. Alternatively, their own living processes may release chemicals that are toxic to us. Strategies for dealing with harmful bacteria depend a great deal on where they occur. Like the useful bacteria, the harmful ones can be found in a variety of places within and on the body, as well as in places such as sinks, drains and the floor – almost anywhere that they can find a source of food. Needless to say, eliminating harmful bacteria from within the human body needs a somewhat different strategy to that for attacking colonies established in drains! In this chapter we will examine the mode of action of some of the various antibacterial agents that are available to us in the constant fight against pathogenic bacteria in all these locations.

## 8.2 Know your enemy

One reason why control of bacterial growth is important is the speed with which an unwanted colony of bacteria can grow if reproduction is unchecked. Bacteria reproduce by growing in size and dividing into two, a process that can take as little as 20 minutes for some bacteria, which means the number in the colony doubles three times in each hour. It can be calculated that, starting with a single bacterium, in just 24 hours it could grow into a colony of over $10^{21}$ bacteria, roughly equal to the NASA (North American Space Agency) estimate of the total number of stars in the Universe!

Of course, this number of bacteria assumes a sufficient food supply and no deaths, which is unlikely to be achieved in practice. The point remains, though, that growth can be very fast, causing rapid development of symptoms, especially the level of pain if the growing colony is trapped, say under a fingernail or tooth, or very serious illness if the bacteria colonise essential organs in the body and interfere with their function.

The structure of a typical animal cell was shown in Figure 4.9, but bacterial cells have some differences. Cells such as that in Figure 4.9 have the DNA and RNA contained within the nucleus, separated from the cytosol, the watery fluid in the cell that contains all the other cell chemicals. Organisms that have cells with a nucleus (e.g. humans) are known as eukaryotes (pronounced 'you-carry-oats'). Single-celled organisms such as bacteria do not have a nucleus – their DNA and RNA is free within the cytosol. Such organisms are called prokaryotes (pronounced 'pro-carry-oats').

Now that bacteria are known to be single-celled organisms it becomes possible to rationalise how some of the original antibacterials, that were applied without much molecular understanding, were able to suppress infection. If you turn back to Figures 4.9 and 4.10 you will recall that the contents of cells are kept in place by a cell membrane. Bacterial cells also have a cell wall which, although porous, is able to strengthen the cell membrane (see Section 8.6.1). Attacking this membrane through the porous cell wall is one way of destroying the bacterium. If the membrane can be weakened, the cell will burst and the bacterium dies. Alternatively, preventing replication of the bacteria can be the aim, allowing the body's own defences time to combat the infection. This can be achieved if some way can be found of preventing enlargement of the cell membrane – the cell will be unable to grow and divide. It will also be unable to replicate if it is prevented from forming new DNA, so again the colony will die out. We will look at all these strategies.

## 8.3   Targeting the cell membrane

Figure 4.10 shows the structure of the cell membrane. It contains molecules that consist of non-polar hydrocarbon tails attached to cationic (positively charged) water-soluble polar heads. These molecules are phospholipids and have a fairly complicated structure (Figure 8.2).

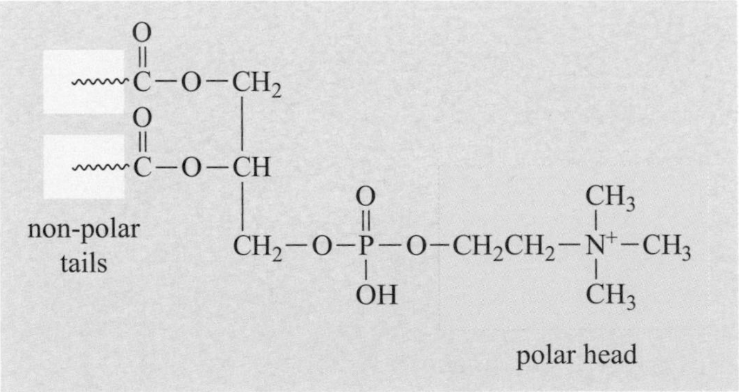

**Figure 8.2**   Structure of a phospholipid, showing the polar head and non-polar hydrocarbon tails.

● Study Figure 8.2 carefully and identify the symbol for an atom that you have not met before.

● It is P. This is the element phosphorus – hence the name phospholipid.

The non-polar tails are attracted together in the membrane by London forces whilst the polar heads are attracted to polar water molecules both inside and outside the cell membrane. Although the cell membrane is very thin (around 5 nm, i.e. 0.000 000 005 metres), the arrangement of the phospholipids shown in

Figure 4.10 makes it strong enough to fulfil its functions, albeit strengthened by an outer cell wall, unless it is weakened in some way. Weakening occurs if the membrane is exposed to molecules that are sufficiently similar to the phospholipid molecules to be able to replace them within the membrane, but different enough to weaken the structure.

Such chemicals are known as surfactants, because they are active at a surface – the useful type here are cationic surfactants, so named because the molecules have an ionic group that is positively charged, just like a phospholipid molecule. If enough surfactant molecules replace phospholipids in the membrane its structure is lost and the cell (the bacterium) dies, usually because it bursts open.

The structures of some typical common cationic antibacterial agents are shown in **8.1** benzalkonium chloride, **8.2** cetrimide and **8.3** cetylpyridinium chloride. The fine structural details of these molecules are unimportant. The important thing is that they all have a long hydrocarbon chain and a cationic group which is a positively charged nitrogen atom (an ammonium cation), similar to the polar part of the phospholipid molecule (Figure 8.2). The resemblance is sufficient for the antibacterial molecules to be able to form London forces to the non-polar chains of the phospholipids and replace the phospholipids in the membrane. This weakens the membrane enough for it to lose its structure.

**8.1** benzalkonium chloride

**8.2** cetrimide

**8.3** cetylpyridinium chloride

A major limitation to the use of cationic surfactants is that they cannot be used for general bacterial infections because, in the same way that they destroy bacteria, they also destroy red blood cells. However, they are useful when the infection is on – rather than in – the body, such as a sore throat, so antibacterials of this type are often found in throat lozenges, such as Merocaine® and Dequadin®, or antiseptic mouthwashes. (Have a look on the labels if you have any such lozenges or mouthwashes tucked away in the medicine cupboard.) When used as such they are termed antiseptics – that is they kill bacteria on living tissues. You will also find them in some disinfectants, which kill bacteria on inanimate surfaces such as sinks, baths and floors.

**Question 8.1**

Which of the following structures would you expect to have antibacterial properties? Explain your answers in a couple of sentences for each.

(a) The sulfonium chloride, **8.4**.

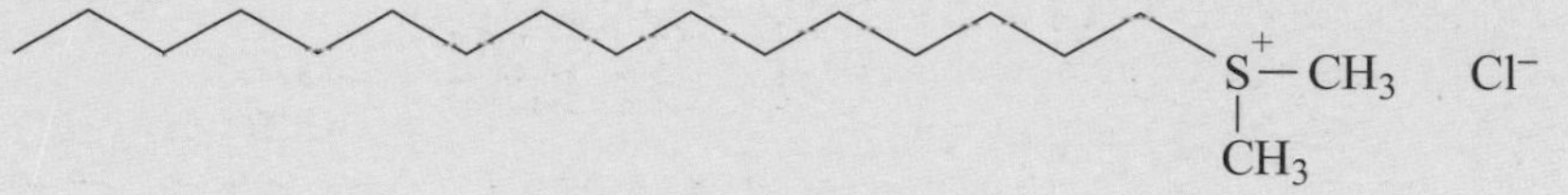

**8.4** sulfonium chloride

(b) The linear alkylbenzene sulfonate, **8.5**.

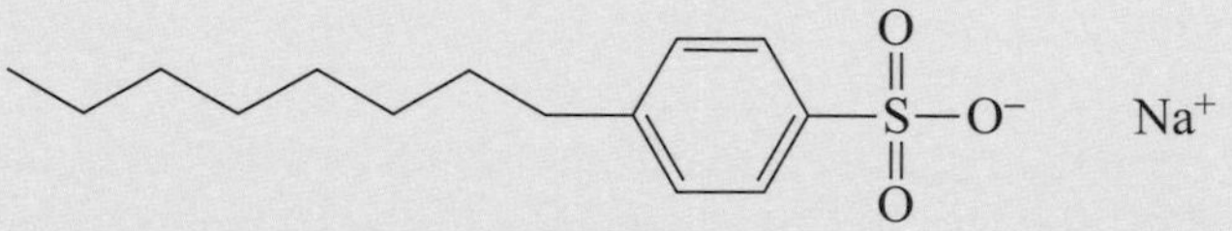

**8.5** alkylbenzene sulfonate

(c) Dodecane, **8.6**.

**8.6** dodecane

# 8.4   Coal-tar, carbolic acid and phenols

Although petroleum has nowadays mainly replaced coal as the raw material for the manufacture of most organic chemicals, there can be few households that do not contain a product that owes its existence to compounds originally developed from those present in 'coal tar' – a thick, black, liquid mixture of many chemicals produced when coal is heated, in the absence of air, in the process to produce coke and coal gas. The liquid antiseptic 'Dettol' is one such product. In the UK, the person most closely associated with exploiting the antiseptic properties of coal tar is Joseph Lister (Figure 8.3).

● Coal-tar is a mixture of a whole variety of compounds. Knowing this, what might you try to do to find out what gives coal-tar its antiseptic properties? (Think back to the general strategy for drug development introduced in Chapter 1.)

● A sensible approach would be to try and separate the various compounds in coal-tar and test them individually for activity.

Coal-tar can be separated into a variety of components simply by heating. The compounds that boil at lower temperatures distil off first and can be condensed and collected, while the higher boiling compounds distil off later as the temperature is increased. (The process is very similar to the process for separating crude oil into its components in an oil refinery.) It turned out that the compound with antiseptic properties was phenol, or carbolic acid as it was called at the time. You first met phenol in Activity 2.1.

**Figure 8.3** Joseph Lister (1827–1912). In 1965 Britain celebrated the centenary of Lister's contribution to the development of antiseptic surgery by issuing commemorative postage stamps. The one shilling stamp is overprinted with an impression of the molecular structure of the major compound responsible for antiseptic activity – phenol.

## Activity 8.1

Make a molecular model of phenol using your model kit. Your model should look like that in Figure 8.4.

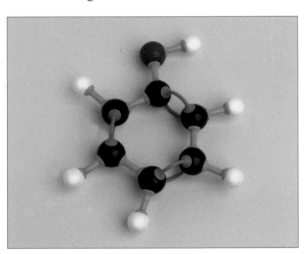

**Figure 8.4** A ball-and-stick model of phenol.

- Now draw the various equivalent ways of representing the two-dimensional structure of a molecule of phenol.

- Any of the structures in Figure 8.5 can be used.

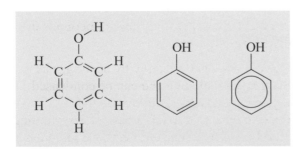

**Figure 8.5** Structural formulae for phenol.

The molecular formula of phenol is $C_6H_6O$, but more usually it is written as $C_6H_5OH$ to show that it contains a benzene ring and the —OH functional group. You should recall from Activity 2.1 that, just to confuse the issue, the —OH functional group is known as a phenol group when joined in this way to a benzene ring, but an alcohol group when attached to other hydrocarbon chains (see Table 2.1 or the bookmark).

### Question 8.2

Look at the representation of the structure of phenol on the Lister stamp (Figure 8.3). It is obviously intended to give an impression of the structure. What is needed to make it a *chemically* correct structure?  ◀

After reading Pasteur's account of how infectious diseases were caused by bacteria, Lister set about finding a substance that would destroy such bacteria and so prevent infection. His choice of carbolic acid arose because he came across a newspaper account of its use to treat sewage in Carlisle. Success was sporadic at first but, with improved techniques of use, the benefits of using carbolic acid as an antiseptic eventually became apparent and Lister became famous as the first person intentionally to use antiseptics in surgery. Carbolic acid (phenol) itself became a widely used disinfectant and antiseptic (Figure 8.6).

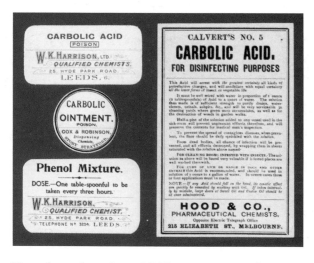

**Figure 8.6**    Labels from products containing carbolic acid (phenol) used in the early 1900s.

How does phenol work? There appear to be two modes of action. First, it denatures the proteins in the bacterial cells. The —OH group on the phenol forms hydrogen bonds to the various proteins that are needed for cell structure and for catalysing the chemical reactions that go on inside the cells. By hydrogen bonding to these proteins it alters their secondary structures (Section 3.3) enough to destroy their biological function. Look again at Section 3.1 if you want reminding of the general structure of proteins.

### Question 8.3

With which groups on the cell proteins might the phenol —OH form hydrogen bonds?  ◀

To help understand the other way that phenol can affect bacteria, have another look at its molecular structure in Figure 8.5. We have already identified the —OH group as being able to form hydrogen bonds, i.e. it is polar.

● What can you say about the polarity of the rest of the phenol molecule?

● It is a hydrocarbon group, so it is non-polar.

● What property does a substance have if its molecular structure has a (non-polar) hydrocarbon fragment at one end and a (polar) water-soluble fragment at the other?

● Such substances act as surfactants.

In addition to denaturing the proteins, phenol damages bacterial membranes partly by disrupting the cell membrane, by acting in a similar way to the cationic surfactants that we discussed earlier. As the polar end of phenol is neither a cation nor an anion, phenol can be regarded as a non-ionic surfactant.

Unfortunately, phenol itself is a rather caustic substance, causing general damage to human tissues as well as targeting bacteria on the tissues. In the UK, proprietary preparations should contain no more than 1% phenol in water; at such concentrations it acts as a bacteriostat (the bacteria are not killed, but the colony ceases to grow in number) rather than a bacteriocide (the bacteria are killed).

**8.7**

● If you assume that increased antibacterial activity is related to its ability to act as a surfactant and disrupt the phospholipids in the cell membrane, in general terms how might you modify the molecular structure of phenol, whilst retaining the —OH group, to generate a new compound that is likely to be a better antiseptic? (*Hint*: look back to the structures of the cationic surfactants **8.1**–**8.3**.)

● Cationic surfactants have hydrocarbon groups with longer chains than phenol, so one possibility might be to increase the size of the hydrocarbon part of the phenol molecule by substituting some of its hydrogen atoms with other non-polar groups.

**8.8**

**8.9**

The cresols, **8.7**, **8.8** and **8.9**, which can also be obtained from coal-tar, have similar antiseptic activity to phenol, but have less general toxicity and so are safer to use. As well as containing an —OH group, these compounds have a —CH$_3$ group attached at varying positions on the benzene ring. Solutions containing cresol and soap are marketed as the antiseptic detergent 'Lysol', used for cleaning and sterilising.

The similar, naturally occurring, compound thymol, **8.10**, present in the essential oil derived from thyme, is also a much more powerful antiseptic than phenol, and is used chiefly in mouthwashes and gargles.

**8.10** thymol

By attaching a longer hydrocarbon chain to the ring, the activity may be increased considerably because the hydrocarbon chains enable these molecules to cause greater disruption to the phospholipid cell membrane. One such compound is *n*-hexylresorcinol, **8.11**. The hexyl term comes from the Greek word for six, and there are six carbon atoms in the hydrocarbon chain. The prefix *n* denotes that, of all the possible isomers for the hexyl group, the one used is the unbranched one. Notice that there is a second —OH group on the benzene ring.

**8.11** *n*-hexylresorcinol

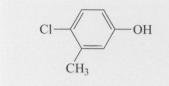

**8.12** chlorocresol

**8.13** hexachlorophane

**8.14** chloroxylenol

**8.15** trichlorophenol

**8.16** eugenol

● Why might a compound like *n*-hexylresorcinol require an extra —OH group in the benzene ring?

● The presence of the longer non-polar hydrocarbon chain reduces the solubility of the molecule in water, because it makes the molecule less polar overall. The second —OH group increases its polarity and the extent of hydrogen bonding to water molecules and so increases its solubility.

● By comparing the features of their molecular structures what limitation might there be to the use of thymol rather than phenol and cresol?

● Thymol contains a three-carbon hydrocarbon chain that is absent in either phenol or cresol. So thymol is likely to be much less water soluble than phenol or cresol.

This is indeed the case; whereas one litre of water at 25 °C will dissolve 83 g of phenol or 20 g of cresol, it will dissolve only 1 g of thymol.

It is often found that the introduction of a covalently bonded chlorine atom (—Cl) into a molecule has a similar effect to introducing long-chain hydrocarbon groups; both tend to increase antiseptic activity whilst also decreasing water solubility. For example, less than 10 g of chlorocresol, **8.12**, will dissolve in a litre of water compared to 20 g of cresol.

Some commonly used antiseptics are hexachlorophane (pronounced 'heksa-kloro-fane') **8.13**, chloroxylenol ('kloro-zile-en-ol') **8.14**, and trichlorophenol ('try-kloro-feenol') **8.15**. Hexachlorophane is used as a disinfectant in medicated soaps, chloroxylenol is used in 'Dettol' and trichlorophenol is the material that gives rise to the name of the antiseptic 'TCP' (Figure 8.7). They are generally referred to as chlorinated phenols or chlorophenols.

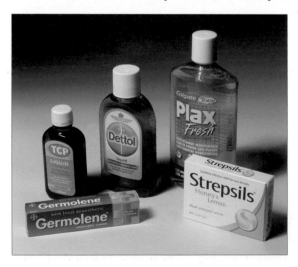

**Figure 8.7**   Some antiseptic products that contain phenol derivatives.

**Question 8.4**

Eugenol, **8.16**, is a compound that can be isolated as the major constituent of oil of cloves. Decide whether or not you might use eugenol as an antiseptic and give your reasons.  ◄

In the next section we will look at some other chlorine-containing antibacterials that have an entirely different mode of action to that of the chlorinated phenols.

# 8.5   Chlorine – a World War I trench warfare gas

Chlorine is a thoroughly nasty substance. It is a yellow–green (hence its name; *chloros* is Greek for yellow–green), dense, choking gas which exists as molecules containing two chlorine atoms joined by a covalent bond: Cl—Cl or $Cl_2$. It attacks the mucous membranes of the eyes, nose, throat and lungs, and causes the lungs to fill with fluid so that the person exposed to it drowns internally. Even a relatively minor whiff of it can cause lung collapse. Chlorine was one of the first chemical warfare agents. Perhaps it is a failure in humans that, given the almost limitless potential for chemistry to improve the quality of our lives, we also use chemical knowledge as an agent of destruction.

Chlorine also provides an excellent example of how properties can change when one chemical is converted into another by a chemical reaction. Chlorine might be a deadly gas, but react it with sodium, Na (a highly reactive metal that bursts into flames when dropped into water), and it becomes sodium chloride, NaCl – common salt, an essential component of our diet.

Chlorine was discovered in 1774 by C. W. Scheele in Sweden. By 1785 the bleaching properties of a solution of chlorine in water had been noted, and by 1788 such aqueous solutions had been recommended as disinfectants after they had been observed to prevent the obnoxious smells caused by decaying organic matter. Dissolving chlorine in water (to form an aqueous solution) reduced the acute toxic effects of the gas but still provided a solution that acted as a disinfectant, killing the bacteria that caused the decay.

It was soon found that the disinfectant properties of the solution were improved if the chlorine was dissolved, not in water alone, but in an aqueous solution of sodium hydroxide (NaOH). The chlorine first dissolves in the water and then reacts with sodium hydroxide to form sodium chloride and sodium hypochlorite (NaOCl), Reaction 8.1.

$$Cl_2(aq) + 2NaOH(aq) = NaCl(aq) + NaOCl(aq) + H_2O(l) \qquad (8.1)$$

The symbols in brackets denote that the substance is in aqueous solution (aq) or is a liquid (l). Other symbols that are sometimes used include (s) for solid and (g) for gaseous. Note that two sodium hydroxides are needed on the left-hand side of the equation in order to balance the numbers of atoms of each element in the compounds involved on either side of the equation.

The solution formed by Reaction 8.1 is the basis of many bleaches and disinfectants, such as 'Parazone' and 'Domestos', which are widely used today. Have a look at the bottle if you have one and you will see that the active ingredient is sodium hypochlorite, NaOCl, usually limited to not more than 5% for safety reasons – remember chlorine is also a trench warfare gas!

## 8.5.1   Bleach as a disinfectant – a molecular explanation

The sodium hypochlorite is present as sodium ions ($Na^+$) and hypochlorite ions ($OCl^-$) and it is the latter that enable the solution to act as a disinfectant. Chlorine in this form is sometimes referred to as 'active chlorine', as it is readily available to take part in chemical reactions, in contrast to relatively unreactive chlorine

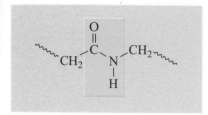

**Figure 8.8**   An amide group in a protein chain.

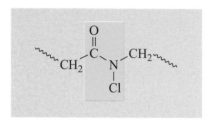

**Figure 8.9**   A chlorinated amide group.

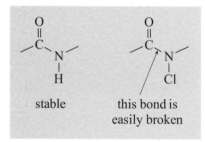

**Figure 8.10**   The effect of chlorinating an N—H in an amide.

atoms covalently bonded in molecules, such as some of the general anaesthetics discussed in Chapter 5 and the chlorophenols discussed in Section 8.4. The sodium ions do not take part in the reaction so are another example of spectator ions (Section 5.2.1).

Bleach disinfects because it reacts with cell proteins that are responsible for cell structure, as well as with the enzyme proteins that are vital to the chemical reactions that take place in the cell. You should recall from Chapter 3 that proteins contain nitrogen atoms in the amide functional groups (Figure 8.8) that link together the amino acid residues in the primary structure of the protein.

The amide groups are particularly susceptible to attack by active chlorine compounds leading to the replacement of the hydrogen atom by a chlorine atom (Figure 8.9).

Such an apparently trivial change has profound chemical consequences. First, the hydrogen atom on the nitrogen is essential for the hydrogen bonding needed in globular protein structure – remove it, by replacing it with chlorine, and the hydrogen bonding is no longer possible. The secondary structure of the protein collapses, the protein has become denatured and it can no longer perform its function of, for example, catalysing the reactions essential for cell maintenance. Second, the presence of the chlorine atom changes the chemical reactivity of the amide group. Whereas the non-chlorinated amide is a stable group, chlorinating it makes it unstable because the C—N bond becomes weakened and is easily broken (Figure 8.10). Breaking the amide bond destroys the primary structure of the protein in just the same way as breaking a link in a chain destroys the chain. Again, the structure of the protein collapses.

Hypochlorites are powerful disinfectants so they are fine for killing bacteria on non-living surfaces, such as sinks, floors, drains, etc. However, they are not particularly satisfactory for cleaning open wounds or delicate tissues. The solutions irritate tissue, as well as attack harmful bacteria, and only very dilute solutions (far less than the 5% of household bleach) can be used for such purposes.

### 8.5.2   Drinking water

Most of this course has focused on chemical ways of treating disease or relieving pain. However, preventing disease in the first place is often easier, very much cheaper and less unpleasant for the people involved. Today, large-scale disinfection of the drinking water supply is carried out by dissolving controlled quantities of chlorine gas in it. This kills potentially harmful bacteria by the chemical reactions that we have described. However, chlorine in the water supply can be a contentious issue. Some people find it gives an unpleasant taste to the water, so choose to drink bottled water. What cannot be in doubt is the vital contribution that a clean, bacteria-free drinking water supply makes to the health of a nation. One only has to look at the mortality rate from water-borne diseases in countries that do not have a regular supply of safe drinking water to be convinced of the importance of this.

The following extract puts the matter into perspective and shows the effectiveness of chlorine as a disinfectant.

'The main consideration in ensuring the safety of public water supplies is the elimination of the agents of water borne infectious disease. In the 20th century major epidemics of typhoid and cholera in Britain and elsewhere in Europe were only eliminated when their bacterial origin was recognised, the contamination of water supplies with sewage was eliminated, and disinfection treatment was introduced. There have been no major epidemics in the UK since the Croydon typhoid epidemic of 1937[*] following which all water supplies were chlorinated.'

R. M. Harrison (ed.), (1992) *Pollution, Causes, Effects and Control*, 2nd edn,
The Royal Society of Chemistry

Of course, bacteria are not the only undesirable potential contaminants in drinking water. There are many toxic chemicals, e.g. lead, nickel and copper compounds, which enter the water supply because they occur naturally in the ground through which the water percolates, or as a result of mining. Others, e.g. benzene, are more likely to find their way into the water supply because of industrial carelessness or accidents. The World Health Organisation (WHO) lays down guidelines for the maximum acceptable concentrations of many potential drinking water contaminants.

Figure 8.11 shows students carrying out laboratory analysis of chemical contaminants in water samples during the Open University Level 1 residential course in practical science. The project examines ways of identifying some of the chemical contaminants that can leach into the water supply from underground sources and determines the concentration of aluminium ions in some typical water supplies, enabling them to be compared with recommended maximum levels.

**Figure 8.11**   The water analysis project at the Open University Level 1 residential course in practical science.

[*] Author's note: Unlike regions where drinking water is not chlorinated, nowadays a typhoid epidemic in Croydon would be almost beyond belief, but 1937 is certainly during many of our grandparents' lifetimes and probably during some of our parents' lifetimes, so well within living memory.

## 8.6   Antibacterial drugs

It is almost impossible to imagine life today without antibacterial drugs to combat illness arising from bacterial infection. A visit to the doctor often results in a prescription for an antibiotic, followed by a cure within a few days, although the cure does not follow if the illness is caused by a virus, as they are not affected by antibiotics. These days, there is a range of different antibiotics available, classified broadly into groups according to common features in their molecular structure. Figure 8.12 shows some of the arsenal of antibacterial medicines available in the war on bad bacteria. You may well have come across some of these.

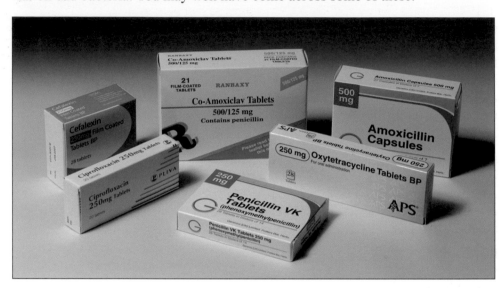

**Figure 8.12**   A selection of medicines containing antibiotics.

However, such a powerful armoury of antibacterial medicines has not always existed. Before 1930 there were few effective means of treating infection. Antiseptics and disinfectants for cleaning surface wounds, inoculation of antitoxins for combating illnesses such as diphtheria, and extracts of certain plants such as echinacea and chamomile which have some antimicrobial activity, were available. There were, however, many diseases caused by bacterial infection for which no effective treatment existed.

Two classes of compound rapidly filled this gap: the penicillins and the sulfonamides. Some penicillins are naturally occurring compounds formed by certain moulds, but most are semi-synthetic, because the compounds formed by the moulds are modified chemically to produce more effective antibiotics. Strictly speaking an antibiotic is a compound that is produced by a microbe, e.g. a mould, which can kill or prevent the growth of another microbe. Sulfonamides are purely synthetic materials and are not found in nature so they are not usually classified as antibiotics although their use is effectively the same. (Sir Winston Churchill was treated successfully for pneumonia with one of the earliest sulfonamides, sulfapyridine, in 1943.)

### 8.6.1   The penicillins

As with so many drug discoveries, penicillin was developed from an entirely chance observation. In 1928, Alexander Fleming (Figure 8.13) whilst working at St Mary's Hospital Medical School in London, noticed that an experiment on bacterial growth had accidentally become contaminated with a green mould that inhibited the growth of the bacteria. The mould turned out to be *Penicillium notatum* and, rather than throw the culture away as a failed experiment, he decided to investigate it further. It was found that a chemical extracted from the mould killed some types of pathogenic bacteria. Most importantly it produced no ill effects when injected into mice and rabbits or eaten by one of his assistants! Fleming called the chemical penicillin. Antibiotics had been discovered.

In 1940 Howard Florey and Ernst Chain showed that penicillin cured otherwise lethal infections in mice and later, after some rather hurried clinical testing, in humans. It was a fortunate time for such a discovery as World War II created a high demand for antibiotics for treating infected injuries. Fleming's work was acknowledged with a knighthood in 1944 and he shared the Nobel Prize for medicine with Florey and Chain in 1945.

**Figure 8.13** Alexander Fleming (1881–1955), the Scottish bacteriologist.

Note the use of the plural in the title to this section. *Penicillium notatum* makes several closely related products which were isolated and called penicillin F, G, K and X. The different penicillins had antibacterial properties which varied depending on which bacterium was exposed to them. By choosing different nutrients in which to grow the mould, production of one or other of the penicillins could be encouraged.

Further research during the 1950s led to the compound 6-aminopenicillanic acid (6-APA), **8.17**, being identified as the compound on which all the penicillins are based.

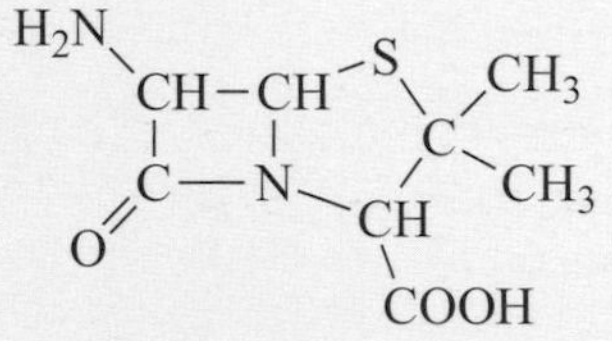

6-APA had almost no effect on bacterial growth but was an important step forward in the development of a range of penicillins. The active penicillins were found to have a side-chain on the amine group, **8.18**, and, by varying the R— group within this side-chain, a range of drugs has become available, with varying activity against different types of infection. We do not need to go into the detailed methods here, but the laboratory reactions to replace a hydrogen atom on an amine with another group (R—CO—) are fairly straightforward, so it was relatively easy to make a range of semi-synthetic penicillins, e.g. penicillin V, by starting with 6-APA and replacing one of the hydrogen atoms on the nitrogen with various groups. (A websearch on 'penicillin' will lead you to a wide variety of structures for both penicillins and the closely related cephalosporins, which have a six-membered ring where penicillin has a five-membered ring.)

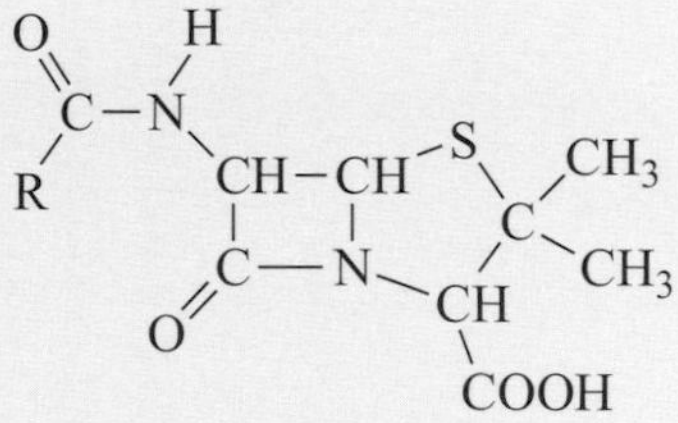

Examples of the R— group on the side-chain are shown in Figure 8.14.

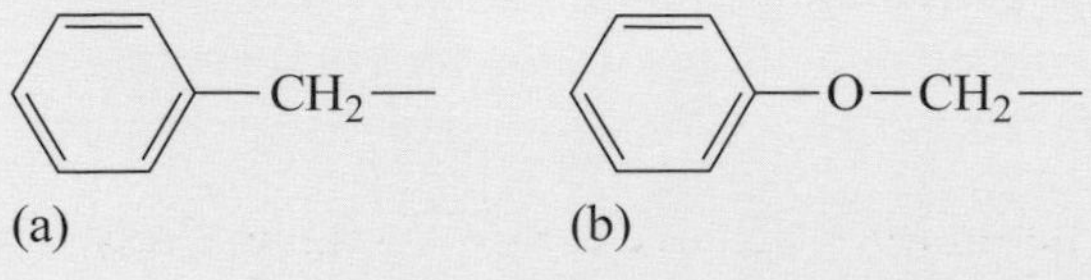

**8.17** 6-aminopenicillanic acid (6-APA)

**8.18** generalised structure of a penicillin

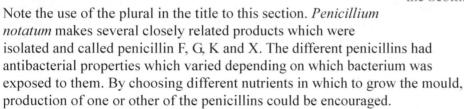

(a)

(b)

**Figure 8.14** Typical R groups in penicillin molecules: (a) gives penicillin G and (b) gives penicillin V.

### How do penicillins work?

In bacterial cells the cell membrane is surrounded and supported by a rigid outer layer known as the cell wall. This consists of a complex structure of polysaccharides and polypeptides. During bacterial replication the cell enlarges and eventually divides into two identical separate cells. As it grows in size the cell needs to make more cell wall. Penicillins block the mechanism for making new cell wall so, as the cell attempts to grow, it bursts and the bacterium dies. A cell that is not replicating is unaffected by penicillin.

● Based on the topics covered in earlier chapters, suggest a general way in which you think penicillin might block growth of the cell wall. (*Hint*: what is often needed to help with chemical reactions in cells?)

● Chemical reactions in cells often make use of an enzyme to catalyse the reaction, so possibly the penicillin in some way blocks the action of, or deactivates an enzyme, that facilitates cell wall growth.

As we have previously seen, enzymes are protein molecules. They frequently have amine groups ($-NH_2$) on side-chains. It appears that the penicillin reacts with an amine on an enzyme that is essential for cell wall growth and deactivates the enzyme.

### Activity 8.2

Make a model of the four-membered ring (also called a β-lactam) of the penicillin molecule – just the three carbon atoms and the nitrogen atom joined by four single bonds will be enough. What do you observe about the ring?

You may have noticed that the bonds are slightly bent (Figure 8.15). This is because the four-membered ring forces the bond angles to be 90° instead of the usual 109.5°.

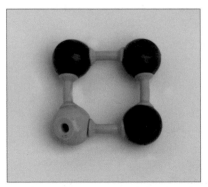

**Figure 8.15**   The β-lactam in the penicillin molecule.

What you have just observed is an example of ring strain. When a molecule is forced to adopt unfavourable bond angles it is said to be 'strained'. This has the effect of making the molecule rather more reactive than is usually the case for similar groups in a larger ring, or a molecule with no ring, with bond angles nearer to 109.5°. When penicillin reacts with an $-NH_2$ group on the enzyme the β-lactam ring opens, so achieving more favourable bond angles.

Reaction 8.2 shows the reaction of penicillin with an $-NH_2$ side-chain on a protein molecule.

- Study Reaction 8.2 carefully. What is the name of the new group that has been formed, shown in blue?

- You should have recognised this as an amide group (Table 2.1 or bookmark).

- The four-membered ring of the penicillin molecule contains an N atom. It has been replaced by an —NH group in the penicillin–enzyme compound. Where has the extra hydrogen atom come from?

- It was one of the hydrogen atoms on the —$NH_2$ side-chain of the enzyme. Look at the reaction again and check that there are no 'lost atoms' or 'gained atoms' that are unaccounted for and that all the valencies are correct. (A standard check when first confronted by an unfamiliar chemical reaction.)

As Reaction 8.2 shows, the new side-chain on the enzyme is now much bulkier than the —$NH_2$ group. Because of the increased size there is insufficient space for it to bind to the reactant molecules, so it is hardly surprising that the enzyme is no longer able to do its job of catalysing the reactions needed for cell wall growth. Compare what has happened with the mechanism by which aspirin deactivates COX and prevents prostaglandin formation (Section 2.8). You will see a pattern emerging: making relatively small changes to molecular structures changes their shape and prevents them from taking part in their usual biological chemical reactions.

### Bacteria's response

As living organisms, bacteria are able to evolve. In Chapter 1 we discussed problems that arise when strains of bacteria evolve that are resistant to our antibiotic armoury. Mutations in their DNA can produce bacteria that have a natural defence against penicillin and are therefore unaffected by it. They can thrive until another more successful antibiotic is found. Of course, the problem gets worse because if we eliminate all the bacteria that do respond to treatment, only those that do not respond are left, and these can flourish even more without competition.

The mechanism for bacterial defence against penicillin involves an enzyme, β-lactamase*, which some bacteria have evolved the ability to produce. The enzyme β-lactamase is able to attach to and open the β-lactam ring of the penicillin. It then releases the former penicillin molecule, which cannot now interact with bacterial enzymes because it no longer has its four-membered β-lactam ring intact. The β-lactamase is then free to deactivate further penicillin molecules.

---

* You will often see enzymes named in the style ending in –ase. This indicates that it interacts with whatever precedes ase in the name. β-Lactamase is sometimes referred to as penicillinase.

**8.19** clavulanic acid

### The Empire strikes back

Humans are a persistent and resourceful species and chemists have discovered that if the β-lactamase enzyme is offered the alternative β-lactam, clavulanic acid, **8.19**, then the β-lactamase will open the four-membered ring of this in preference to reacting with penicillin, leaving the penicillin still available to inhibit cell wall growth. Although clavulanic acid is not itself antibiotic, when mixed with penicillin, e.g. in the antibiotic Co-Amoxiclav® (Figure 8.12), it enables the penicillin to deal with bacteria which would otherwise prove resistant.

**Question 8.5**

It seems that the β-lactamase problem could be avoided if penicillin is *always* mixed with clavulanic acid before use. Why is this not done? ◄

**Question 8.6**

(a) Draw a reaction, similar to Reaction 8.2, which shows an enzyme's —NH$_2$ group reacting with a molecule of clavulanic acid (remember to check that all the valencies are correct and no atoms have been unintentionally lost or gained).

(b) What is the new functional group that has been formed?

(c) Why do you think clavulanic acid does not have antibiotic properties? ◄

### 8.6.2   The sulfonamide drugs

How could a purely synthetic compound be developed as a very important antibacterial when no naturally occurring lead compound existed to provide the initial clues? The answer can be traced back to the genius of Paul Ehrlich (Figure 8.16) who established the discipline of chemotherapy.

Ehrlich spent the early part of his career studying the way cells could be stained for microscopic examination. A modern example of this is shown in Figure 8.17. Ehrlich's interest took a novel direction when, instead of removing tissue from animals and then staining it, he injected the dyes into living animals and allowed dyes to diffuse into the tissues before the tissues were removed for examination. This apparently simple idea had a profound affect on the understanding of how chemicals are dispersed throughout the body.

**Figure 8.16**   Paul Ehrlich (1854–1915), the German bacteriologist.

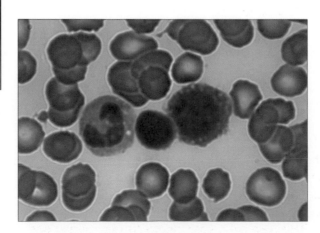

**Figure 8.17**   Light micrograph of red blood cells and three white cells (stained blue). The nucleus is clearly visible in one of the white cells. Staining enables the cells to be distinguished.

Gradually, this led Ehrlich to propose the idea that therapeutic compounds acted upon the cells to which they were bound, or in the case of dyes, stained. This idea proved to be the beginnings of theories about drug–receptor interactions that we discussed earlier when finding out about cocaine. He discovered, for example, that the dye methylene blue selectively stained nerve fibres. This led him to propose that it might have analgesic (pain-relieving) activity. (It does, but it also causes kidney damage.) This work eventually led to him proposing the concept of a receptor for a molecule. He is remembered for his pioneering work in the understanding of how molecules interact with biological tissues and in the use of 'magic bullet' chemicals aimed at specific biological targets.

Ehrlich's work with dyes led the German pharmacologist Gerhard Domagk, together with chemists Fritz Mietzsch and Joseph Klarer, to test a range of azo dyes when they set out to discover a drug that would be effective against bacterial infection. Azo dyes are brightly coloured organic compounds (Figure 8.18). Their structures are characterised by two benzene rings linked by a nitrogen–nitrogen double bond (the azo group, —N=N—), as in, for example, the orange dyestuff chrysoidine, **8.20**.

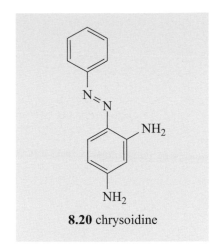

**8.20** chrysoidine

Among the many thousands of azo compounds tested were those that contained the sulfonamide group (Figure 8.19). Work concentrated on these because it was known that the sulfonamide group enabled the dyes to bind strongly to wool, which is a protein. It was not unreasonable to suppose that if the group enables the dyes to have a high affinity for wool, then it might also confer high affinity to the proteins of microbes.

When sulfonamide compounds were injected into mice that had been infected with a virulent strain of bacteria, *Streptococcus pyogenes* (the bacterium responsible for the deaths from pneumonia during the worldwide influenza epidemic of 1918–19), they were found to be particularly effective in protecting the infected mice. One compound, **8.21**, subsequently marketed as Prontosil®, was found to be active in clinical trials in humans and Domagk even used it successfully to treat his own daughter, who had developed life-threatening septicaemia after pricking her finger on a needle.

**8.21** Prontosil

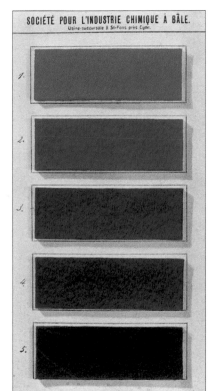

**Figure 8.18** Textiles dyed with azo compounds.

**Figure 8.19** The sulfonamide group.

So here was a lead compound. But why does it work? What molecular features should be varied? One puzzle that required solving was the observation that Prontosil is active against bacteria in animals (*in vivo*, i.e. in living things) but not against bacteria in test-tubes (*in vitro*, literally means 'in glass'). Why? Perhaps Prontosil is transformed into an active compound in animals but not by bacteria in laboratory apparatus. This idea led other workers to suggest that one

**8.22** sulfanilamide

such breakdown product might be sulfanilamide, **8.22**, which can be formed from Prontosil by breaking the azo linkage and adding two hydrogen atoms. Indeed, sulfanilamide can be found in the urine of patients treated with Prontosil. When sulfanilamide was tested for bactericidal activity in its own right, it was found to be as active as Prontosil itself.

### Question 8.7

Write an equation that identifies the other product when Prontosil reacts with four hydrogen atoms to form sulfanilamide. As in all equations, make sure all the atoms are accounted for. ◄

Sulfanilamide then became the lead compound, but how did it work? Which molecular features of this compound could be varied? We will first explore how answers to the question about its mode of action were unravelled.

Unlike Prontosil, which is brick red, sulfanilamide is a colourless substance, so clearly the concept of needing a *dye* to interact with cellular proteins is incorrect. Even so, perhaps sulfanilamide still binds in some way to these proteins, but how? Several important observations can be made. Although sulfanilamide is a powerful antibacterial, sometimes it is ineffective, particularly if the infection is surrounded by pus. Similarly, in laboratory experiments, the antibacterial activity of sulfanilamide is diminished if pus is added. Yeast can have the same effect.

● What might you infer from these observations?

● A couple of possibilities come to mind; either sulfanilamide has a greater affinity for pus than for the bacteria, or the pus (or yeast) contains a substance that inhibits the action of the drug.

By focusing attention on a yeast compound, two relatively simple reactions were able to provide important clues as to how the effects of sulfanilamide can be inhibited. First, the compound reacts with alkali. This property is characteristic of acids, so it would appear that the material that inhibits sulfanilamide is an acid. Second, treatment of the compound with nitrous acid ($HNO_2$) destroys its ability to inhibit sulfanilamide. The reaction with nitrous acid is typical of amine groups, particularly those in which the amine group is directly attached to a benzene ring, e.g. **8.23**, aniline (systematic name, phenylamine); the simplest compound with an amine group attached to a benzene ring. The reaction with nitrous acid removes the amine group, so the loss of activity demonstrates the amine group to be important.

**8.23** aniline

Combining these two observations led to the suggestion that the inhibiting substance present in yeast is *para*-aminobenzoic acid (PABA), **8.24**, which has both a carboxylic acid group and an amine group on the benzene ring.

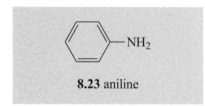

**8.24** *para*-aminobenzoic acid (PABA)

Indeed, PABA can be isolated from yeast and is essential for the growth of bacteria – it acts as a kind of 'bacterial vitamin'. Administration of PABA and sulfanilamide together protects bacteria against the action of the sulfonamide drug: the more sulfanilamide present, the more PABA that is required. It seems the two compounds compete for some process essential to the growth of bacteria. This seems reasonable if we compare the structures of the two substances, **8.22** and **8.24** which have considerable similarity.

To be able to explain how sulfanilamide works we need to know the role that PABA plays in the growth of bacteria. PABA is one of three essential constituents that are used to make folic acid (Figure 8.20). Don't worry about the complex structure of folic acid; we are only interested in noticing that PABA is needed to link pteridine alcohol and glutamic acid together when folic acid is formed.

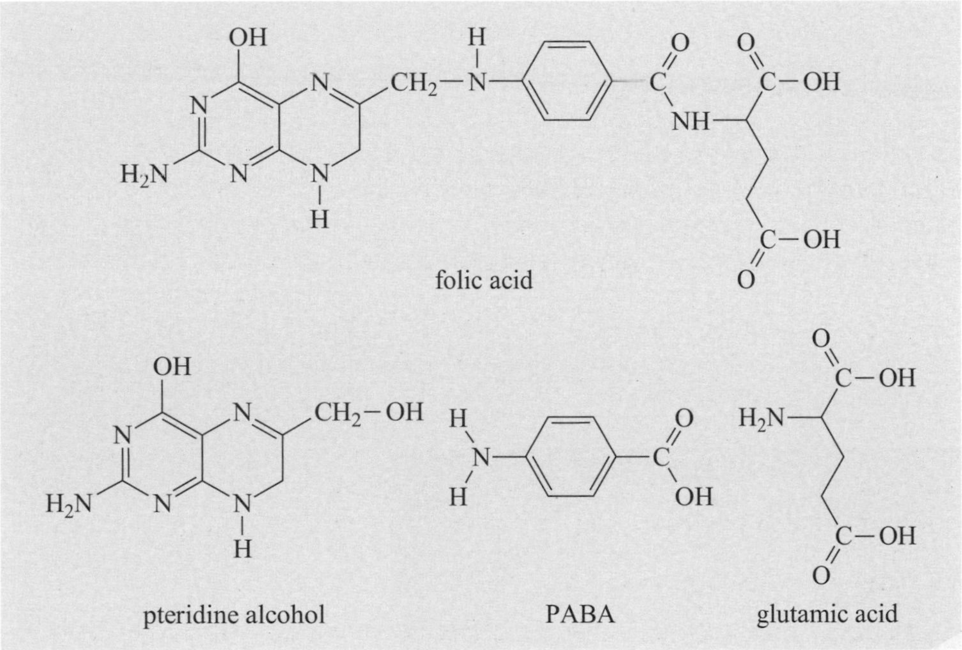

**Figure 8.20** The relationship between PABA and folic acid.

Folic acid is absolutely essential to the growth of bacteria because it enables them to synthesise DNA, which they must do if they are going to replicate. Bacteria contain several enzymes that enable them to make folic acid from the three constituents, PABA, pteridine (pronounced 'ter-id-een') alcohol and glutamic ('glue-tam-ick') acid. One enzyme is needed to link PABA and glutamic acid together, to form an intermediate, glutamylPABA. Other enzymes are needed to activate the pteridine alcohol, so that it can react with glutamylPABA. A final enzyme takes the activated pteridine alcohol and glutamylPABA and links them together to form folic acid. It is this enzyme with which sulfonamide drugs interfere. The details of the structures are unimportant – the important thing is to appreciate that it is an enzyme that is involved in the synthesis of folic acid, in the scheme outlined in Figure 8.21.

It would appear that sulfanilamide and the other sulfonamide drugs sufficiently resemble glutamylPABA for the enzyme to accept them in competition with glutamylPABA. There is only one site to occupy per enzyme molecule so, if sulfanilamide occupies it, then glutamylPABA cannot do so. This means that the formation of folic acid is blocked.

Unable to synthesise any more DNA, the bacteria cease replicating. Though each bacterial cell is still viable, the progress of the infection stops. This gives the natural defence

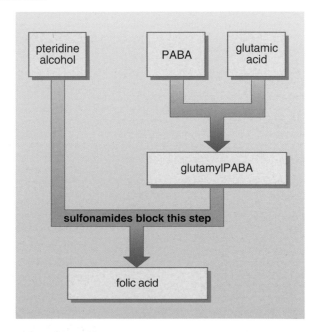

**Figure 8.21** Steps in the formation of folic acid.

**133**

mechanisms of the body – antibodies (proteins produced by white blood cells to render foreign substances harmless) and phagocytes (cells that are able to engulf and break down foreign bodies) – a chance to destroy the remaining bacteria and the patient can recover.

● So, are sulfonamides bacteriocidal or bacteriostatic?

● Since they do not destroy bacteria, but only arrest their growth, they must be bacteriostatic.

It may have crossed your mind that humans also need to synthesise DNA, so why are sulfonamides not toxic to us? The reason lies in the different ways humans and bacteria get their folic acid. Humans, like bacteria, need folic acid for DNA synthesis. Indeed, for humans folic acid is a vitamin, an essential dietary component that is needed in small amounts to ensure good health. But, unlike bacteria which have to synthesise folic acid, we get ours ready made from our diet. Green vegetables, potatoes, offal and yeast extracts (Figure 8.22) are all sources of folic acid. Even cornflakes are nowadays fortified with folic acid, amongst other vitamins.

**Figure 8.22**   Some dietary sources of folic acid.

We need to take in folic acid in our diet because we lack the enzymes needed to make it. Only bacteria have the enzyme that sulfonamides inhibit, so bacteria are sensitive to sulfonamides while we are not. But why do the invading bacteria not use the folic acid that we ingest from our food? It is because, although bacteria are able to make folic acid, they have not developed a mechanism for absorbing existing folic acid into their cells. So we can eat all the folic acid we want, but the bacteria cannot use it. Sulfonamides are really very selective drugs indeed and exploit a difference in the metabolisms of humans and bacteria.

Once it was understood how sulfonamides work, attention could be turned to the question of what molecular features of sulfanilamide can be varied to provide more effective drugs. It turns out that most of the sulfanilamide molecule is essential, but a range of drugs can be made by substituting one of the hydrogen atoms on the $-NH_2$ group attached to the sulfur atom, for example sulfapyridine, **8.25**, the sulfanilamide drug that was used to treat Sir Winston Churchill's pneumonia. Although nowadays sulfonamides have to a large extent been replaced by other antibacterials, e.g. the penicillins, they are still used for treating some human infections, for example of the urinary tract, and in veterinary medicine.

**8.25** sulfapyridine

The development of an understanding of how sulfonamides work was a landmark in medicinal chemistry because it was the first explanation of drug action at the molecular level. For his work on the development of sulfonamides Domagk was awarded the Nobel Prize for Medicine in 1939, but because of the complications of living in war-torn Europe he was unable to accept it until 1947.

### 8.6.3 A possible future addition to the antibacterial arsenal

To round off your study of antibiotics you should find it interesting to listen to the radio programme, *Frontiers – the New Antibiotics*, that is on CD2.

The programme starts with a warning given by Alexander Fleming in 1945, about misuse of penicillin and then reviews the problems caused by bacteria acquiring resistance to the traditional antibiotics such as those you have just read about. The recording then presents a completely new possible way of dealing with bacterial infections, before relating back to some of the ideas in Box 1.1 of Chapter 1.

## 8.7 Summary of Chapter 8

In this chapter you have learnt that:

- Phenol (carbolic acid) can be obtained from coal-tar by distillation. Phenol is a derivative of benzene, containing a six-carbon atom benzene ring attached to an $-OH$ group.

- Phenol has antiseptic properties because it can denature proteins by forming hydrogen bonds to them as well as by acting as a non-ionic surfactant. Phenols that contain hydrocarbon groups attached to the benzene ring have enhanced surfactant and antiseptic properties.

- Cationic surfactants have antibacterial properties because they can enter the cell membrane and weaken it, so the cell bursts and dies.

- Bleach is a solution containing sodium hypochlorite and sodium chloride. Hypochlorite ions contain active chlorine, which is able to replace hydrogen atoms of amide groups in enzymes and proteins with chlorine atoms. This alters the hydrogen bonding properties and chemical reactivity of the amide groups and destroys the biological function of the enzymes and proteins.

- Antibacterial drugs can be developed that interfere with specific enzyme-catalysed processes.

- Penicillins can inhibit bacterial replication by preventing cell wall formation, achieved by rendering an enzyme ineffective.

- Some bacteria can make penicillins ineffective by producing β-lactamase.

- Clavulanic acid is not an antibiotic but its β-lactam group can react with β-lactamase, making the latter unavailable for disabling the penicillin molecule. Clavulanic acid can be mixed with penicillin when it is used against β-lactamase-producing bacteria.

- Sulfonamide antibacterials were developed following observations on azo dyes. They work by interfering with the enzyme-catalysed reactions that bacteria use to make folic acid, needed for DNA synthesis.

- Sulfonamide drugs have no effect on the replication of human cells because humans are able to utilise dietary folic acid.

## 8.8  Reflection

Now that you have completed another chapter we suggest you again pause to reflect on how things are going. In particular we hope you noticed:

- the common mode of action (attack on the cell membrane or cell wall) of phenol, chlorine and penicillin, but

- the entirely different mode of action of sulfonamides. Leaving aside the rather complicated structural chemistry in the sulfonamide story, the overall effect is to prevent growth of the bacterial colony by interfering with DNA synthesis.

# Drugs for viruses

Many of the diseases from which humans suffer are caused by microorganisms (microbes), notably bacteria and viruses. As we saw in the last chapter, bacteria are single-celled organisms with all the necessary biological apparatus to enable them to reproduce (including both deoxyribonucleic acid (DNA) and the related molecule ribonucleic acid (RNA)).

Viruses are quite different from bacteria. They are an order of magnitude (which means a factor of ten) smaller and consist of a core of nucleic acid surrounded by a protective protein and phospholipid envelope (Figure 9.1). The nucleic acid is either DNA or RNA, but no virus is yet known that contains both. Viruses do not carry out any biochemical reactions such as synthesising proteins or metabolising nutrients to provide energy. Most crucially, although the DNA or RNA contains the information necessary for reproduction, viruses are unable to multiply by themselves. Instead, the virus acts like a parasite and needs to infect a living, susceptible host cell. It then takes over or 'hijacks' the host's 'chemical workshop', appropriating the necessary components for its own purposes. The host cell then manufactures new virus particles according to the instructions provided by the original virus. Because viruses do not engage in metabolic processes of their own, they are not susceptible to antibiotics or indeed to many other types of drugs. In most cases, all that can be done to treat virus-caused diseases is to alleviate the symptoms and allow the body's own immune system to deal with the viral infection in due course. We need only think of the treatment of the viral infection we call the 'common cold' as an example of this approach.

Interest in viruses has greatly increased in recent years because of the implication of the Human Immunodeficiency Virus (HIV) in the development of Acquired Immunodeficiency Syndrome (AIDS). The huge publicity generated by AIDS has had the effect of relegating other viruses to relative obscurity although they are still very much a problem and the diseases they cause cannot be effectively combated. Yet there is one extremely well-known disease caused by a virus, which before AIDS hit the headlines, was described as 'the last great plague'. That disease is influenza, more commonly known simply as 'the flu'.

envelope

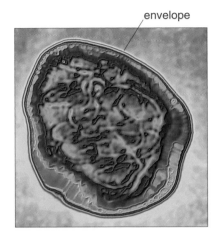

**Figure 9.1** Coloured transmission electron micrograph of a measles virus. The virus is surrounded by an envelope composed of phospholipid and protein. The envelope also contains protein factors which promote infection of further host cells. Within this envelope is seen a purple mass of protein containing the genetic material of the virus.

## 9.1   The influenza virus

Influenza has been present for much of recorded history. One of the earliest epidemics occurred in Greece and was reported by Hippocrates in 412 BC. The Italians introduced the name 'influenza' during an outbreak of flu in 1504 in the belief that it was caused by the influence (*influenza* in Italian) of the stars, though later writers make reference to *influenza di freddo* (influence of the cold). It has been known since the 1930s that viruses cause influenza. Most people reading this will be well aware of the symptoms of flu. Giving rise to an elevated temperature and muscular aches and pains, flu tends to be regarded more as a nuisance than a life-threatening disease. Yet each winter many older people and small children are killed by flu or the other diseases that people contract as a result of flu. In years when there is an epidemic, many thousands die. In the1918 epidemic, more correctly called a pandemic (see below), flu and the pneumonia associated with it was responsible for more deaths in a short time than any other cause: some 20 million people died. This of course occurred before the discovery of the antibiotics that would almost certainly have dramatically reduced the death toll due to pneumonia.

As with other viral diseases, there is no cure currently available. There isn't even a very effective treatment for flu. Even the proven anti-flu drug, amantadine (marketed as Symmetrel®) is only effective against a limited number of strains of the virus and in recent years even these strains have developed a resistance to the drug. One of the reasons why flu is particularly difficult to treat is that new strains are constantly appearing. When only a minor variation in the virus occurs, most of the population has antibodies in their immune system from a previous outbreak, such as in 1993 in Britain (Figure 9.2). If a more substantial change in the virus has taken place, then the population has insufficient antibodies and an epidemic can occur. When a completely new strain appears, a severe and widespread epidemic can occur which is given the name pandemic. The pandemics of the 20th century occurred in 1918, 1957 (Asian flu) and 1968 (Hong Kong flu). At the time of writing (2006) the possibility of the transfer of a particularly virulent form of avian flu to humans is being given serious attention.

Vaccination against flu can be carried out and although only partially effective it is sufficient for the National Health Service (NHS) in the UK to encourage older people and others at risk to have an annual flu jab, and for many employers to pay for mass vaccination of employees as a cost-effective way of

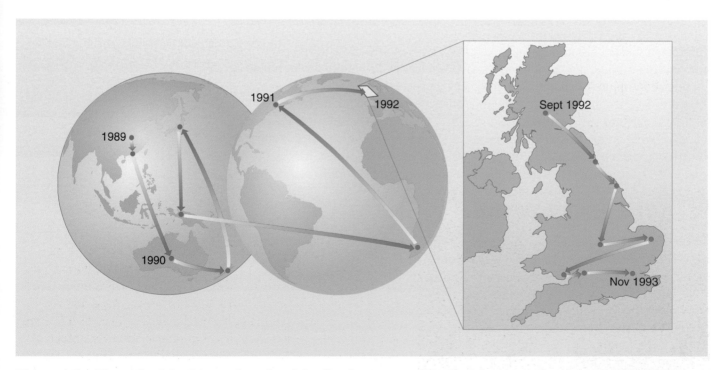

**Figure 9.2**   The path of the *Beijing A* strain of the flu virus responsible for the 1993 outbreak in the UK from its source in China in 1989. There are three main types of influenza: A, B and C. C is generally mild but both A and B can cause widespread epidemics. The full title of the 1993 UK strain is A/*Beijing/32/92*, which identifies its type, place of origin, virus structure and the year it appeared.

reducing sick leave. However, the vaccine is made to counter *previous* strains of flu. By its very nature, the next strain is unknown, so vaccines are always one step behind. The search for drugs that cure or at least provide effective treatment has been underway for many years, mainly by the trial-and-error method of screening possible compounds. However, although this approach has been remarkably successful at discovering drugs to treat other diseases, little progress in finding a cure for flu has been made by this route.

## 9.2 Getting to know the enemy!

The flu virus is roughly spherical in shape (Figure 9.3) and contains a core of RNA within a protein and phospholipid envelope (Figure 9.4). The whole virus is covered by hundreds of spikes of two different types, each type being made up of a particular protein. One type, called haemagglutinin, has a vital role in the first stages of infection, the penetration of host cells. Each haemagglutinin spike has a number of pockets at its end. These pockets are receptor sites for attaching the virus to the outside of the host cell membrane. They recognise a particular feature, a molecule called sialic acid, **9.1**, which is found on the membrane of susceptible cells within the body, such as those within the respiratory tract.

The sialic acid molecule is chemically bound to the cell membrane of susceptible cells and fits the receptor site in the haemagglutinin spike, thereby enabling the flu virus to attach itself to the cell prior to penetration.

**9.1 sialic acid**

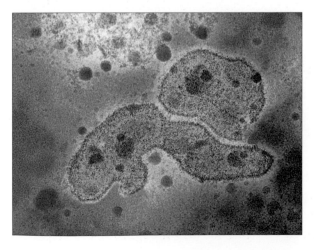

**Figure 9.3** Transmission electron micrograph of an avian influenza virus. This virus was isolated in Vietnam, during the avian flu outbreak in early 2004. The virus consists of ribonucleic acid (RNA), surrounded by an envelope of phospholipid and protein (green). The natural hosts of this virus are wild birds, which show few symptoms; however, infected domestic birds suffer a 90–100% mortality rate. Humans that have contact with infected birds can become infected, but at the time of writing (2006), no human-to-human transmission has yet been recorded.

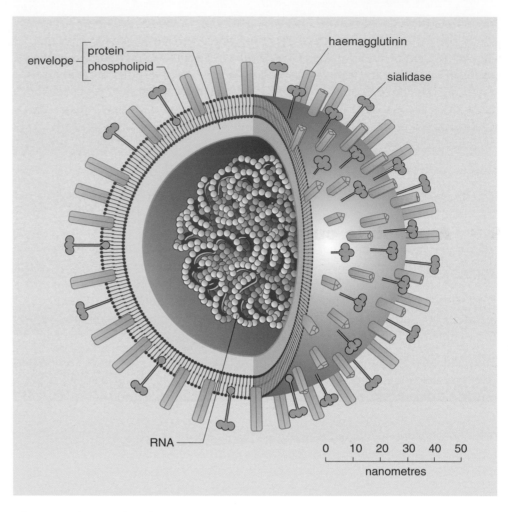

**Figure 9.4**   Schematic diagram of an influenza virus.

The second type of spike shown in Figure 9.4, called sialidase, is an enzyme.

● What, in general, is the function of an enzyme?

● Enzymes are proteins that catalyse reactions. Enzymes are usually quite specific as to the substances that they transform.

The specific role of the sialidase enzyme seems to be to help newly formed viruses to escape from the host cell and spread to other cells in the body. They are then able to move on and infect other cells. As part of this process, sialidase cleaves off sialic acid groups (hence the name 'sialidase') from the membranes of the host cells. As with the haemagglutinin spikes, the sialidase spikes also have pockets that are the active sites for the enzyme activity and into which the bound sialic acid fits during the cleavage process. So, just as we have seen before in the course, we have an enzyme with an active site for binding to its substrate (sialic acid).

This should prompt an idea of how effective drugs might be developed.

If we can block the sialidase enzyme the new virus will have no means of removing itself from the host cell. Haemagglutinin would still bind the virus on the surface of its host, thus trapping the virus and preventing its spread to other cells.

The structure of the active site in the deeper recesses of the sialidase protein pockets seems to remain constant across the various influenza strains. What varies in the different major strains of the influenza virus is the amino acid sequences of the sialidase proteins that surround the active site in the various flu strains. It is for this reason that natural antibodies or vaccines are only partially successful: they interact with the surface of the sialidase protein rather than the inner parts of the pockets that constitute the active sites. Any effective anti-influenza virus drug must take account of this fact.

**Question 9.1**

Why is it so difficult to find a successful drug to treat influenza? ◀

## 9.3  A possible cure for influenza

In the search for such effective anti-influenza drugs, some researchers have concentrated on the initial infecting action of haemagglutinin. Other groups have focused their attention on sialidase and this is the story we will pursue.

● Given that sialidase is an enzyme, what type of compound should be sought that might act to prevent infection from spreading?

● A compound that inhibits the action of sialidase, that is a kind of molecular 'plug' of the type we have met elsewhere in this course, which could occupy the active site of the enzyme in preference to the sialic acid group. Once the enzyme is 'plugged' (blocked), then the newly formed viruses would be prevented from escaping from the host cell and spreading to other cells.

As you saw in Chapter 7, a compound that plugs or blocks the action of an enzyme is called an inhibitor. Sialidase inhibitors have been sought for many years but without much success. In attempting to design an inhibitor, an obvious place to start is with the structure of sialic acid itself.

● Why do you think the sialic acid structure is a good starting point?

● Since the sialic acid group is the natural substrate in the cell, it is known to bind to the active site of the sialidase enzyme. A sialidase inhibitor would also need to bind to the active site, so using the sialic acid structure as a starting point should increase the chances of discovering a molecule that binds strongly.

One such synthetic derivative of sialic acid called Neu5Ac2en (pronounced 'new-five-ack-two-enn'), **9.2**, was reported in 1969. It is essentially a molecule of sialic acid, which has lost a molecule of water to give a double bond adjacent to the carboxylic acid group. Neu5Ac2en was shown to inhibit the action of sialidase. Unfortunately, it does so only weakly, so large doses would be required if it were to be used as a drug. Even more worryingly, Neu5Ac2en was not very specific. Other sialidase enzymes occur in bacteria and in mammals, and Neu5Ac2en was shown to inhibit the action of these enzymes to a similar extent to that found with influenza sialidase. Finally, Neu5Ac2en only acts as an inhibitor *in vitro*, in other words in the test tube, and not *in vivo*, that is in living systems, thus making it useless for treating disease, no matter how large the dose!

**9.2** Neu5Ac2en

Many similar compounds related to Neu5Ac2en were synthesised over the years using the trial-and-error method, but none was a significantly more effective inhibitor, and none was shown to be effective *in vivo*. Given the nature of this kind of research to find an effective drug, this sort of failure would be expected in the planning process. No wonder that successful development of new drugs can cost a fortune.

**Question 9.2**

Explain in your own words why a sialidase inhibitor would be expected to act as a drug against influenza. ◀

## 9.4   Use of computers in drug design

Clearly an entirely different approach was needed. This was made possible when a research group at the CSIRO Division of Protein Chemistry at Victoria in Australia managed in the early 1980s to determine the detailed molecular structure of the influenza sialidase enzyme using the technique of X-ray crystallography.

In addition to determining the structure of the enzyme itself, the researchers took a crystal of the enzyme sialidase and 'soaked' it in sialic acid by immersing the enzyme in a solution of the acid. Some of the sialic acid molecules migrated to the active site in the enzyme. By determining the structure of the enzyme with the substrate molecule in place, the Australian scientists were able to find out exactly how the sialic acid was positioned in the active site. Then by soaking the enzyme in Neu5Ac2en they were also able to determine the structure of sialidase with the inhibitor molecule in place. Reassuringly, they found that the way in which the inhibitor occupied the active site was very similar to the way in which sialic acid was bound.

With this information, it was possible to examine the 'pocket' in which the sialic acid or inhibitor resides in more detail. This is precisely what a group of Australian scientists did with the additional involvement of scientists working in the UK for the pharmaceutical company GlaxoSmithKline.

The first aim was to see if there was additional space in the pocket to accommodate various different molecular groupings that could be attached to the Neu5Ac2en template. Then the researchers wanted to see what amino acids in the enzyme were adjacent to these positions on the template so they could decide which new groups added to the Neu5Ac2en might bind to the pocket.

Careful examination of the active site cavity with sialic acid bound in place revealed that there was indeed space for fitting other groups. The results are shown in Figure 9.5a. To help you identify the sialic acid molecule in the active site of the enzyme, a model of the molecule is shown in Figure 9.5b. Once it had been determined that space was available, the question was how to decide which additional groups would be most suitable. As an aid to this process, they used a computer program called GRID that had been developed at Oxford University in the mid-1980s.

The method gets its name from the fact that the calculations are carried out for each of a regular array of points (a three-dimensional 'grid') that covers the

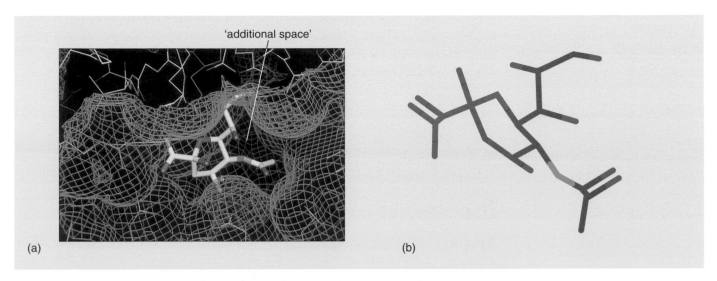

**Figure 9.5** (a) The structure of sialidase showing the sialic acid molecule bound in the pocket that is the active site of the enzyme. The 'blue net' represents the surface of the enzyme that is accessible in and around the pocket and the 'additional space' for extra molecular groups is shown slightly to the right of the sialic acid molecule. (b) A model of sialic acid. This model is a skeleton of the molecule that does not show hydrogen atoms. To enable a useful comparison to be made, it is orientated in the same way as the sialic acid in the active site of the enzyme in (a).

whole of the protein molecule. Using the GRID method it is also possible to discover those locations on the surface of the protein where there is a net attraction for a particular group, called a 'probe group'. Such a location is called a 'hot spot' and signifies a potentially favourable binding site for a molecule containing that particular probe group.

The interactions between the probe group and the protein molecule are treated as being made up of a sum of the individual contributions from the various forces that the probe group can experience. These are the kind of forces that lead to the weak interactions between molecules that we have discussed throughout the course. Dipole–dipole attractions, London forces and hydrogen bonding all come into play.

The Australian team first of all tested the GRID program by using a carboxylic acid probe group to investigate the sialidase active site. Sure enough, a 'hot spot' was duly found precisely where the sialic acid carboxylic acid group sits when it binds to the enzyme.

Careful inspection of a model of the sialidase active site with the inhibitor Neu5Ac2en in place enabled the team to spot a nearby glutamic acid residue (Glu 119) close to one particular hydroxyl (—OH) group on the inhibitor. Glutamic acid has a free carboxylic acid group, —COOH, which can lose an $H^+$ to form a carboxylate ion (—$COO^-$) which could strongly attract an —$NH_2$ group that has gained $H^+$ to form an ammonium ion (—$NH_3^+$). When a fresh GRID calculation was carried out, this time using an amine (—$NH_2$) probe, a hot spot appeared exactly where one was expected. The presence of other amine hot spots from the GRID results, together with further visual inspection, revealed an additional glutamic acid residue (Glu 227) potentially within reach. The numbers 119 and 227 refer to the exact position of the glutamic acid residues in the

guanidino group

enzyme chain. These results provided the vital clue the Australian chemists needed. They designed and synthesised guanidino-Neu5Ac2en, **9.3**, in which an —OH group of the original inhibitor was replaced by a guanidino group (see margin), which is effectively a bigger group.

**9.3** guanidino-Neu5Ac2en
(zanamivir)

The excellent match between guanidino-Neu5Ac2en and the GRID-calculated hot spots can be seen in Figure 9.6.

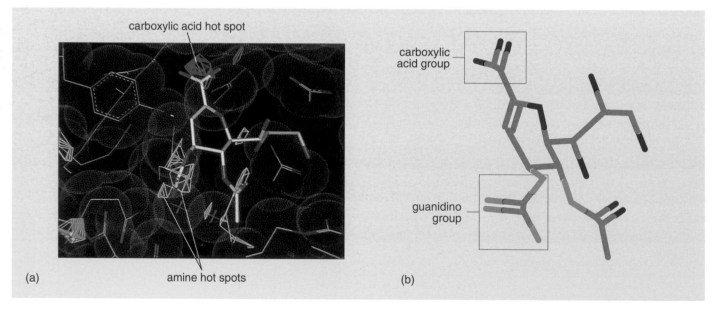

(a)

carboxylic acid hot spot

amine hot spots

(b)

carboxylic acid group

guanidino group

**Figure 9.6**   GRID results for the sialic acid active site in sialidase with guanidino-Neu5Ac2en in place. The dotted blue-mauve spheres and pale skeletal structures are parts of the sialidase structure. The red shape shows the carboxylic acid hot spot lying exactly where the carboxylic acid group of guanidino-Neu5Ac2en inhibitor is located; the various blue shapes are amine hotspots, two of which match up with the location of the ends of the guanidino group. (b) For comparison, a skeleton model of guanidino-Neu5Ac2en orientated in the same way as it is in (a).

## 9.5   Good chemistry – but limited application!

*In vitro* tests of the guanidino-Neu5Ac2en showed that it was bound to the enzyme at least 5000 times more strongly than Neu5Ac2en itself. Furthermore, the compound now known as zanamivir seemed to be much more selective for influenza virus sialidase than was Neu5Ac2en, and to bind much more weakly to other types of sialidase.

**144**

These initial results alone provided vindication for the approach taken, namely basing the rational design of a new inhibitor on detailed knowledge of the active site of the enzyme. But even more encouraging was the fact that subsequent tests showed the compound to be active *in vivo* as well. Zanamivir showed dramatic inhibition of viral replication, both in tissue cultures (cells grown in a dish on the laboratory bench) and in ferrets infected with influenza virus (Figure 9.7).

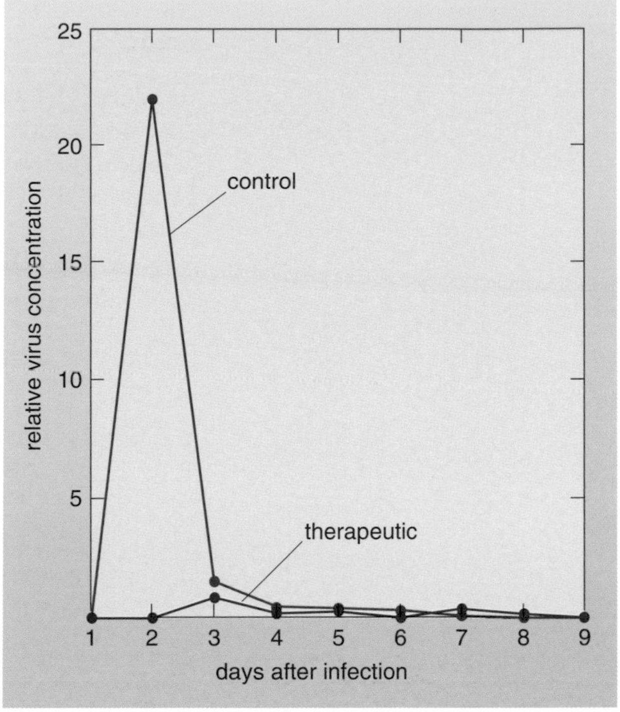

Zanamivir was marketed by GlaxoSmithKline in the US as Relenza®. Whilst zanamivir proved to be a potent and effective inhibitor of influenza sialidase and inhibitor of influenza virus replication *in vitro* and *in vivo*, this didn't necessarily translate into a successful clinical treatment for influenza.

By 2004, just five years after its introduction, the sales of zanamivir had dropped dramatically. Unfortunately widespread use revealed that it was able to reduce the time patients displayed flu symptoms by only 1.5 days and only if treatment with the drug was started within 48 hours of the onset of symptoms. Also the drug was administered by inhalation and this was not acceptable to many in the community.

**Figure 9.7**   Results of the application of zanamivir to ferrets infected with the flu virus. The red line denotes the group that received therapeutic doses of the trial compound; the blue line denotes the control group that were treated with just distilled water.

## 9.6   A star is born

At the same time as zanamivir was being developed, another drug that is a potent inhibitor of sialidase called oseltamivir was discovered which could be administered orally. The drug is currently marketed by Roche under the trade name Tamiflu® (see Figure 1.1). Oseltamivir was widely used during the avian influenza epidemic in south-east Asia in 2005. In response to the epidemic, various governments – including those of the United Kingdom, Canada, United States and Australia – have stockpiled quantities of oseltamivir in preparation for a possible pandemic. Though large, the quantities stockpiled may not be sufficient to treat the entire population of these countries should a pandemic occur.

With increasing fears about the potential for a new influenza pandemic, oseltamivir has received substantial media attention. In early 2005, Roche announced a production shortage of Tamiflu. According to Roche, the major bottleneck in Tamiflu production is the availability of shikimic acid, **9.4**, the starting material for the synthesis of Tamiflu. Shikimic acid cannot itself be synthesised economically and is only effectively isolated from Chinese star anise, an ancient cooking spice. A shortage of star anise is one of the key reasons why there was a worldwide shortage of Tamiflu in 2005. Star anise is grown in four provinces in China and harvested between March and May. It is also produced in Lang Son province, Vietnam. The shikimic acid is extracted from the seeds in a very costly ten-stage manufacturing process. Thirteen grams of star anise make 1.3 g of shikimic acid, which can be made into ten, 75 mg capsules of Tamiflu.

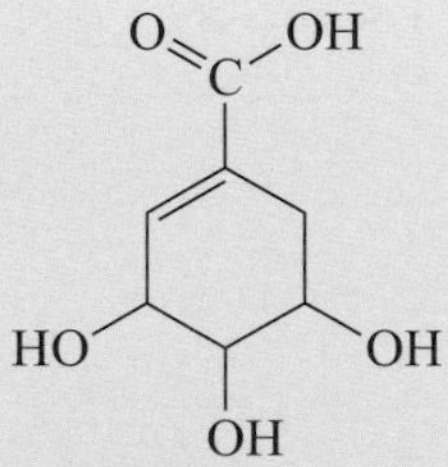

**9.4** shikimic acid

Ninety per cent of the harvest of star anise is already used by Roche in making the drug.

At the time of writing (2006) some academic experts and other drug companies are disputing the difficulty of producing shikimic acid by means other than star anise extraction. Other potential sources of shikimic acid include ginkgo and sweetgum trees. There is an alternative and very appealing method for production of the shikimic acid involving fermentation of glucose by genetically modified *E. coli* bacteria, which is under investigation. There is still work to do if we are to be able to treat a flu pandemic in the future.

**Question 9.3**

Study the structure of oseltamivir, **9.5**, carefully, and compare it with that of zanamivir (guanidino-Neu5Ac2en), **9.3**. What are the similarities and differences in the ring structures of both molecules? ◀

**9.5** oseltamivir (Tamiflu)

There are two points to note about the way in which the drugs we have discussed in this chapter were discovered. First, the information obtained from the structure determination using computers and the GRID program was not of itself sufficient to design the new inhibitor drugs. Experience of this area of research, together with some chemical intuition, was still required to know where in the active site to look and what groups to use to make a viable molecular structure for the drugs. Researchers also needed to have the practical skills to make the compounds once the desired molecular structures had been elucidated. The second point is that both the computer work and the calculation of the GRID data are only approximations. There was no certainty that the new compounds would necessarily turn out to be better inhibitors in practice and as we have seen zanamivir proved to have limited use. But what the method does is greatly to increase the likelihood of success compared with the traditional trial-and-error approach.

This story of the discovery of new inhibitors for influenza virus sialidase is but one example of the application of computer-based molecular modelling in the design of novel (i.e. new and interesting) biologically active compounds. In addition to the use of the modelling computer program, it also involved the use of other software in processing the X-ray crystallography data and in calculating the GRID data. It serves to show how the application of computers in chemistry has transformed the way in which the development of new drugs is carried out. Such is the power of these methods that pharmaceutical companies worldwide are investing heavily in the currently available technology.

**Question 9.4**

In Chapter 7 you saw how the drug captopril was designed as an inhibitor to compete with angiotensin I for angiotensin-converting enzyme (ACE) in the absence of any direct structural information about the ACE active site. List the steps required if you were to attempt to design an improved ACE inhibitor using the approach adopted in the design of guanidino-Neu5Ac2en as a potential drug against influenza. ◀

**Question 9.5**

If the procedure discussed in Question 9.4, was followed, what do you think the chances are of being successful in designing a significantly improved drug compared to captopril? ◀

# 9.7 Summary of Chapter 9

In this chapter you have learnt that:

- The use of computers has found wide application, in the search for new drugs.

- Many of the diseases from which humans suffer are caused by microbes, notably bacteria (see Chapter 8) and viruses.

- One extremely well-known disease caused by a virus that has no really effective drug to cure it is influenza. Vaccination against flu can be carried out but is only partially effective.

- The search for drugs by the trial-and-error method of screening possible compounds has made little progress for influenza drugs. Sialidase inhibitors have been sought for many years but without much success.

- Oseltamivir was the first orally active sialidase inhibitor to be commercially developed as Tamiflu.

- It is important to note that in the design process, though molecular modelling played a vital role it was not simply a mechanical process. Experience of this area of research with some good chemical intuition was still required, together with the skills necessary to make the compounds. This method does greatly increase the likelihood of success compared with the traditional trial-and-error approach.

# 9.8 Reflection

Take time to study the structures of the molecules that we have discussed in this chapter as well as the work we have developed in earlier chapters about the role of weak interactions in enzyme–drug interactions. Look back at the earlier material if you think that may help.

# 10 Whatever next?

Our developing story of how chemistry plays a role in maintaining our health has revolved around the way in which new materials or compounds that have beneficial effects are first of all discovered and then developed into more powerful and useful agents.

Because of the limitations of space in a 10-point course we have had to be selective in choosing the drugs and chemicals to discuss. However, we hope you have become aware of how similar many of the stories are behind the development of quite different drugs.

● Try to recall two ways in which lead compounds have been identified.

● In general the most common way is to isolate a lead compound from a plant or other naturally occurring material. A similar process is to test novel synthetic compounds for biological activity and to use those with promising activity as lead compounds. A more recent method that you have studied is to identify the biological target and to design compounds that contain molecular features that the researchers hope will allow them to interfere with the target and thus prevent the undesirable processes that depend upon the target functioning properly.

Given that there is a vast range of medicines currently available to treat a whole gamut of diseases, it seems appropriate to ask, 'Why is so much effort still put into drug discovery?' and 'How is the role of chemistry in health going to develop in the future?'

## 10.1   The fight goes on

The first question can be answered in several ways. One reason for the need to continue to develop new drugs against infectious diseases, for example, is that the bacteria or viruses can evolve resistance to drugs in current use. This is the particularly worrying present-day situation with regard to antibiotics and is  discussed in *Frontiers – the New Antibiotics* radio programme on CD2. We are beginning to see bacteria that are resistant to all the known types of antibiotic. This happens because a strain of bacteria is not homogeneous. The individual bacteria are not all identical in the same way that all humans are not identical. So when an infection is treated only the susceptible cells are killed off, leaving the resistant cells to replicate. Continued use of one type of antibiotic, or repeated use of different antibiotics can eventually lead to super-resistant strains. This is why there is concern about the overuse of antibiotics and why general practitioners of medicine are often reluctant to prescribe antibiotics for low-grade infections. There is also concern about the excessive use of antibiotics in animals that are part of our food chain.

There are several ways in which bacteria may develop resistance to drugs targeted at enzymes. Two examples you have studied serve to illustrate the problem. Resistance to the sulfonamide drugs, for example, arises because the bacteria can step up their production of PABA, with which sulfonamides compete (Section 8.6.2). This enables the bacteria to produce sufficient folic acid to start multiplying again. In contrast, resistance to penicillins has arisen because the resistant bacteria produce a drug-destroying enzyme, β-lactamase (Section 8.6.1).

Another reason for continued drug development is that although some of the available drugs provide successful treatments, they are not perfect. Salbutamol is a good example (Section 6.6). This drug is an effective treatment for asthma, but it needs to be taken three or four times a day. It would seem inconceivable that salbutamol should not be made available while a drug that needs less frequent administration like salmetrol was being developed. Indeed, as we have seen, it is using a combination of both drugs that has altered the treatment of asthma. For other illnesses it is a better understanding of the chemistry involved that drives continued drug development. For instance, stomach ulcers occur when the underlying layers of the stomach wall are exposed to the acidic secretions of the stomach following localised erosion of the mucous membrane.

● Given this information, what kind of substances do you think might alleviate stomach ulcers?

● Since it is the acidic secretions that are partly responsible, neutralising the acid by alkaline materials ought to alleviate the condition.

Indeed, for many years the main treatment of stomach ulcers relied on the use of medicines to neutralise the acid in the stomach. Even today these medicines are used to 'settle an upset stomach'. Materials that act as alkalis such as magnesium oxide (milk of magnesia), magnesium trisilicate, aluminium hydroxide (Aludrox®) and sodium bicarbonate are common ingredients of antacid preparations because they react with and neutralise acids. Unfortunately, for acid neutralisation to occur throughout the day unrealistically large quantities of these materials are required. Once it was known that the naturally occurring compound called histamine was partly responsible for the secretion of acid in the stomach, a different approach became possible. Histamine acts by binding to receptors on the cells that produce hydrochloric acid. Drugs that block this action of histamine suppress acid production, giving the body an opportunity to repair the mucous membrane lining of the stomach and heal the ulcer. By 1976 SmithKline Beecham had used this approach to develop the anti-ulcer drug Tagamet®, followed in 1981 by Glaxo's Zantac®. Not only are these two drugs very effective treatments for stomach ulcers, they are also two of the most profitable drugs worldwide.

Some drugs that are developed for a specific purpose are found to have unexpected beneficial effects. One that has hit the headlines during recent times is sildenafil. This was developed by Pfizer in their laboratories at Sandwich, Kent as a prospective treatment for hypertension and angina but was eventually marketed, under the brand name Viagra®, in 1998 as an aid to overcoming erectile dysfunction (ED). As over 50% of men above the age of 40 experience some level of ED, it is not surprising that in just a few years Viagra has become so well known and is an extremely profitable product for Pfizer. Although the benefits to so many people and their partners are clear enough, another perhaps unplanned outcome of the availability of Viagra is that it has led to improvement in the general health of many men. Available only on prescription, Viagra has resulted in trips to their GPs by many men who would otherwise have remained in ignorance of the underlying health problem, e.g. diabetes or narrowing of the arteries, of which ED was the first symptom.

Of course, there are diseases that are still without a cure. Many forms of cancer fall within this category. Because cancer cells and normal cells differ very little, any drug that is able to destroy cancer cells will usually destroy normal cells. Drugs used to treat cancer are often very toxic, and need to be administered with care. As with other treatments unpleasant side-effects may develop. So the need to develop improved, more selective drugs goes on, as it does for drugs to deal with those new diseases to which we are exposed, such as AIDS.

Drug development is not just a philanthropic exercise, however. While many of the scientists attracted to work in this field do so out of a genuine desire to create new compounds of benefit to the general well-being of humankind, there can be no doubting that there is a fortune to be made in discovering a novel medicine that can capture a niche in the market. Pharmaceutical companies are enormous wealth-generators, making a significant contribution to the gross national product.

## 10.2 Developing drug design

The answer to the question about the future direction of drug development is that it seems to lie partly along conventional lines, and partly along lines that will develop as we obtain more detailed knowledge about the molecular structures of the biological targets. The conventional method will continue to make use of the compounds that can be isolated from naturally occurring materials, either from animals and plants or from microbes such as yeast or bacteria. It is not unknown for employees of pharmaceutical companies to collect soil samples from their travels around the world so that the microbes contained in them can be grown and examined for any interesting biological properties! Most pharmaceutical companies also continue to have an interest in herbal remedies and in testing tropical plants, hoping to identify important new lead compounds. For example, two compounds that have become mainstays of treating childhood leukaemia and Hodgkin's disease are the anticancer drugs, vincristine and vinblastine. Both are isolated from the Madagascar periwinkle plant *Catharanthus roseus* (Figure 10.1a). Another plant, *Artemisia annua* (Figure 10.1b), is used to treat malaria. This plant contains artemisinin, a compound that has very important antimalarial activity, especially as it is active against parasites that are resistant to the drugs currently in use.

Cone snails that live on coral reefs use their venom to immobilise prey, such as fish, molluscs and worms. These animals harpoon their prey with pointed tongues that are shaped like hypodermic needles. The snails then pump their prey's flesh full of toxins. The potency and complexity of the venom fascinates scientists. Over millions of years cone snails have evolved toxins that target specific species in specific environments. No one toxin is exactly like another. Scientists are studying how each toxin from these animals affects its victim. The results are improving our understanding of how cells, such as those that make up the nervous system, interact and communicate. The research is also leading to the development of new drugs.

(a)  (b)

**Figure 10.1**  (a) *Catharanthus roseus* and (b) *Artemisia annua*, two plants that contain compounds of pharmaceutical value.

Consider, for example, the powerful painkiller ziconotide, the cone-snail-venom-derived drug that was approved for use in the USA in December 2004 and by the European Commission in February 2005. The painkiller (brand name: Prialt®) is injected through a special pump into the fluid surrounding a patient's spinal cord. The drug blocks nerve channels in a similar but not identical way to the local anaesthetics mentioned in Chapter 4. Unlike opium-derived painkillers, such as morphine, ziconotide is said to pose a low risk of addiction and has few side-effects.

Needless to say there is much concern within the pharmaceutical community at the widespread loss of tropical rainforest and coral reefs as well as other environments containing animal and plant species that have never been tested. For example, of the estimated 250 000 different flowering plants believed to be in existence, only some 5000 have been tested for their pharmaceutical attributes.

As we saw in our discussion of influenza drugs the more 'high-tech' route for drug development lies in establishing the precise three-dimensional molecular structures of potential biological targets. These structures can be fed into a computer and visualised on screen. Using the computer, drug molecules can then be precisely designed, and moved around on-screen to see how well they will fit into the active parts of these biological targets. Without going to the effort of synthesising hundreds of compounds and testing each one, using computer modelling it becomes possible to modify molecular structures on screen until the fit of the drug to its target is optimal. Then drug synthesis can begin and although the challenges for the chemist doing this synthesis still remain, at least the work is more focused on a well-designed target molecule. Another possibility is to build into the computer model a way of representing the intermolecular interactions that the molecules experience as they approach each other. This is a bit like the forces that you can feel when you bring two magnets near to each other. As molecules are moved towards the target structure, the interactions between the two can be investigated. This will help in the design of molecules by optimising the interactions we have discussed in this course *before* any compound is made in the laboratory. An extension of this development – one that seems very exciting – is the use of virtual reality in which it will be possible for the drug designer to visualise the molecular world of the biological target. It will be possible to walk around and inside the three-dimensional structure in order to identify potential binding sites as well as to get a better picture of how the drug molecules will fit into their binding site.

## 10.3   Drug delivery

We have not spent much time in this course discussing the formulation of medicines and how they are delivered, although we have mentioned several times the fact that drugs can be administered by injection, orally or as an inhalant. Many of you will be aware of some new formulations that are changing the conventional delivery of drugs, e.g. patches to help smokers with their nicotine dependence while they try to 'give up the habit' and patches too for oestrogen hormone replacement therapy. Implants for the controlled delivery of contraceptive drugs and even anti-schizophrenic medication, as well as slow release capsules and tablets are all recent developments. This area of research and development will undoubtedly become more sophisticated and such topics as nanotechnology (technology in miniature that reflects the scale of our molecules), the use of antibodies to carry drugs, lipospheres (molecular structures that can encase drugs and enable them to be delivered in a controlled manner) and high-velocity powder injections will radically change the way that drugs and medicines are formulated and delivered to patients.

## 10.4   Postscript

Now that you have almost reached the end of the course you could listen again to the four radio programmes on the CDs. With an understanding of some of the chemistry involved you should be able to listen at a somewhat different level to the first time and recognise references, albeit sometimes rather brief, to many of the topics that we have discussed in the course. No doubt there will be future radio or television programmes that will be of interest.

There can be no doubting that chemistry can make a major contribution to issues of health and disease. Yet in your study of this course you may have begun to feel a little uneasy that, underlying drug development, there is a rather reductionist view of how our bodies work, regarding them simply as assemblies of individual components. In the same way that a garage mechanic mends a car – by replacing worn or broken parts, greasing the joints, fine tuning the electrical circuitry – drug development seems to be based on being able to understand illness as due to specific molecular causes – an enzyme that isn't working or a process that is not controlled properly. Given what we know about drug side-effects, and that drugs are not a panacea for all ills, this approach may seem too optimistic. That is a fair, though not entirely justified, criticism.

The benefit derived from the development of antibiotics is one example of the success of the approach. Here, specific molecular events in the life cycle of the invading bacteria are the targets. Drugs for treating high blood pressure – such as captopril – and antiulcer drugs – such as Zantac® – have also grown out of a molecular understanding of the illness for which they are prescribed. Yet we might legitimately ask: 'What causes the high blood pressure and stomach ulcers in the first place?' and we are unlikely to receive an answer couched solely in molecular terms.

It is highly probable that physical and mental stress are likely to figure largely in any response, as, no doubt, would diet and life-style. So the drugs are often treating the consequences of an underlying problem rather than treating the causes. Though there are drugs that can be used to alleviate the illness with greater or lesser success, it is quite clear that drugs alone are unlikely always to be of lasting benefit. Our environment, our way of life and all the things we consume contribute to our state of health. As a society we have become much more aware of this in recent years, and there is a desire to embrace a holistic approach rather than the reductionist approach to health care. The holistic approach considers the whole body and its environment rather than just focusing on one part of it that has gone wrong. This approach leads to treatment of illness through an assessment of each person's individual environment, their way of life and their genetic make-up. The latter is likely to become increasingly important as genetic research expands our knowledge of what it is that makes each one of us unique. Choice of therapy is likely to become much more reliable as knowledge of an individual's genes enables the best available drug for a cure to be chosen more scientifically and with a greater chance of success.

Of course, drugs and medicines can only play one part in the treatment and avoidance of ill-health and disease. Already society is showing a desire to make our environment healthier – in the UK the use of lead-free petrol and the ban on smoking in public buildings being just two examples of recent developments that should reduce ill health.

It is likely that there will be many more.

But that's another story…

# Answers to Questions

**Question 1.1**

There are three different compounds illustrated. A, C and E are the same. B and F are the same. D is the third type.

The approach here is to look for compounds that are superimposable on each other. Making models is a great help and you can short cut this by initially just making the carbon chains. If these are not superimposable there is nothing to be gained by putting other atoms on the chains – they will still not be superimposable. Don't forget that atoms and groups of atoms can be rotated about the bonds that join them to the rest of the molecule.

**Question 1.2**

The answer is $3 \times 10^{13}$ molecules.

(That's 3 with 13 zeros after it, or 30 million million or 30 thousand billion). As suggested in the question, this is a very large number of molecules, so observations on even as small a mass as $10^{-9}$ g of methane are indeed at the macroscopic level.

The calculation goes as follows:

If each molecule of methane has mass $3 \times 10^{-23}$ g, we need to see how many times this divides into the total mass of methane which is 1 ng ($10^{-9}$ g).

So, the number of molecules is $(10^{-9}\,g) \div (3 \times 10^{-23}\,g)$ which is $3.33 \times 10^{13}$.

But the question asks for an answer to 1 significant figure, which gives us $3 \times 10^{13}$ molecules.

(Remember to look in the *Maths Skills Booklet* if you are not sure about significant figures.)

Other common ways of depicting $(10^{-9}) \div (3 \times 10^{-23})$ are

$(10^{-9})/(3 \times 10^{-23})$   or   $\dfrac{10^{-9}}{3 \times 10^{-23}}$

(If clumsy numbers are obscuring the logic, a useful trick is to try the calculation with simple numbers to make it clearer – if there were 10 g of methane and each molecule weighed 2 g, it is fairly clear that our 10 g must contain five molecules. The above calculation is a re-run of this, but with different numbers.)

**Question 2.1**

In Figure 2.17 the ester groups are highlighted in blue.

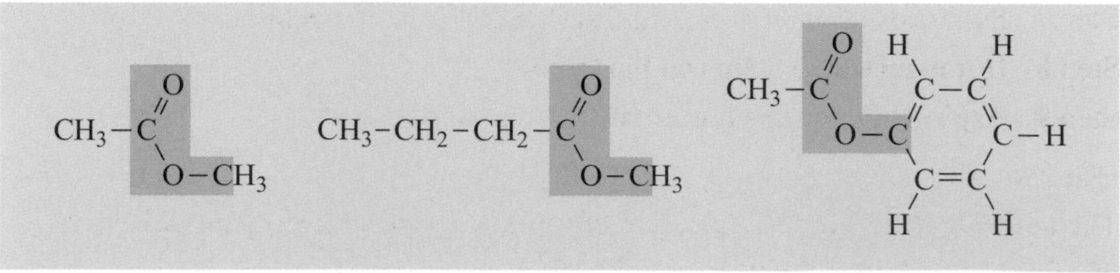

**Figure 2.17**   Ester groups.

Reaction 2.4 shows the generalised equation for the formation of esters (in a slightly different form from Reaction 2.2).

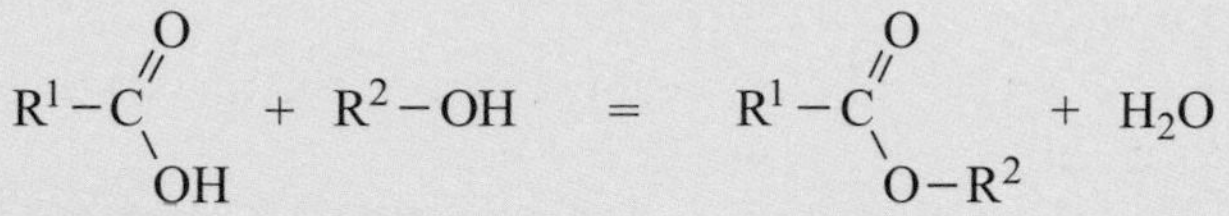

$$R^1 - C\big(\!\!\!\!\overset{O}{\underset{OH}{}} + R^2 - OH = R^1 - C\big(\!\!\!\!\overset{O}{\underset{O-R^2}{}} + H_2O \qquad (2.4)$$

Reactions 2.5 to 2.7 show how each ester would be formed using this reaction.

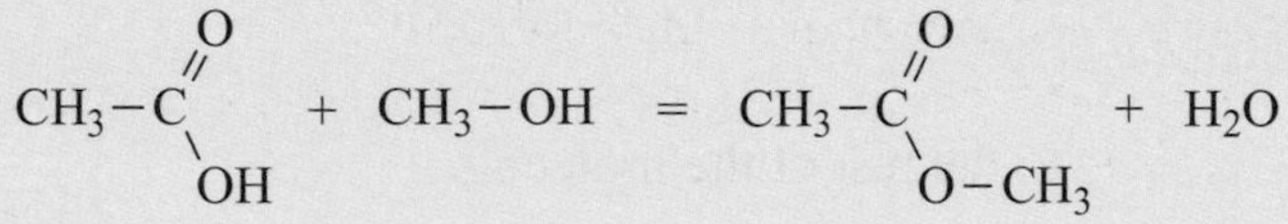

$$CH_3 - C\big(\!\!\!\!\overset{O}{\underset{OH}{}} + CH_3 - OH = CH_3 - C\big(\!\!\!\!\overset{O}{\underset{O-CH_3}{}} + H_2O \qquad (2.5)$$

$$CH_3 - CH_2 - CH_2 - C\big(\!\!\!\!\overset{O}{\underset{OH}{}} + CH_3 - OH = CH_3 - CH_2 - CH_2 - C\big(\!\!\!\!\overset{O}{\underset{O-CH_3}{}} + H_2O \qquad (2.6)$$

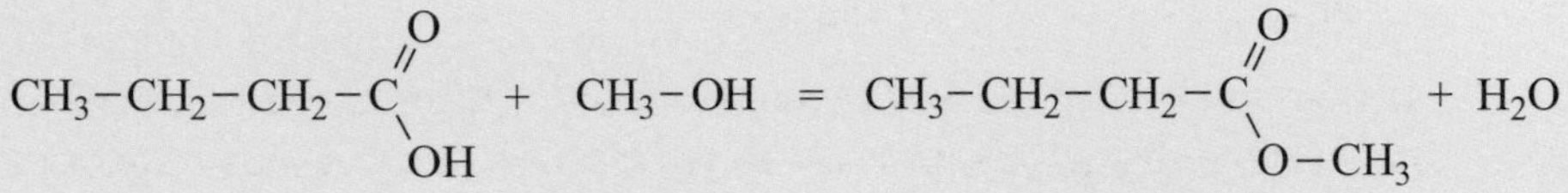

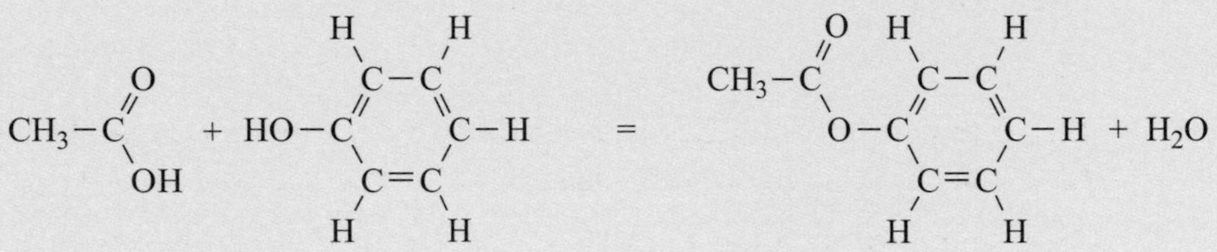

$$(2.7)$$

## Question 2.2

The steps in Figure 1.3 are matched to the development of aspirin as shown below. There are likely to be perfectly acceptable answers that show slight variations.

Step 1   Willow bark and leaves known to be effective painkillers for thousands of years. Salicin extracted from willow bark during the 1840s.

Step 2   Salicin (lead compound) tested and found to be the active ingredient in willow bark and leaves.

Step 3   Structure of salicin investigated.

Step 4   Salicylic acid synthesised.

Step 5   Salicylic acid found to be effective but irritant.

Step 6   Sodium salicylate made. Effective for pain relief, not irritant but tasted awful.

Step 7   Synthesis of other compounds related to salicylic acid.

Step 8   Hofmann tested them (on his father).

Step 9   Aspirin emerged as the suitable compound.

## Question 2.3

The molecular formula just tells you how many atoms of each type there are in one molecule of the compound, so for aspirin it is $C_9H_8O_4$.

(There are six C atoms in the ring plus three in the side-chains, giving nine overall. There are four H atoms attached to the ring carbons that do not carry side-chains plus four H atoms in the side-chains, so a total of eight. There are two O atoms in each side-chain, making four in all.)

**Question 2.4**

You should have found that all the atoms in the benzene molecule lie in one plane, but this is not so with cyclohexane. This is because cyclohexane does not have any double bonds, so repulsion between the bonds keeps the cyclohexane molecule with all its bond angles close to 109.5°, the tetrahedral angle. If the cyclohexane molecule is squashed flat, some of the bonds get closer together. It is the repulsion between these bonds that returns the cyclohexane molecule to its original shape, with all the bond angles equal to 109.5°, when it is no longer held squashed flat.

**Question 2.5**

Enzymes are highly specific in their action. That is to say each enzyme will only catalyse a very small range of chemical reactions, or perhaps only one. As a human cell needs to carry out a very great number of different reactions it needs a wide range of different enzymes. It only needs a small amount of each enzyme because enzymes are not used up or converted into different chemicals when they perform their function of catalysing cell reactions, so are recycled.

**Question 3.1**

Reactions 3.5 to 3.7 show the reaction of each amino acid to give a chain containing four leucine amino acid residues. Notice that the chain still has an amine group and a carboxylic acid group for further reaction.

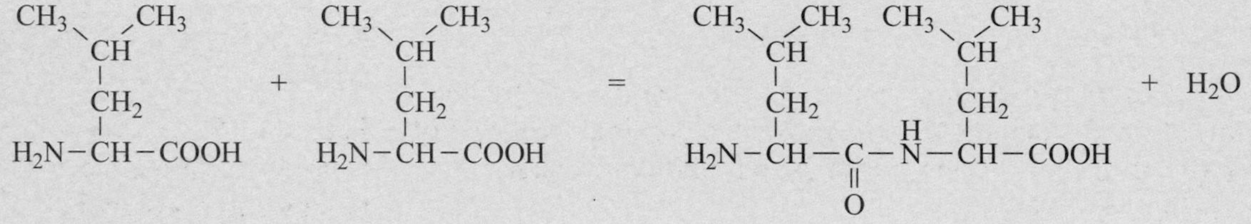

(3.5)

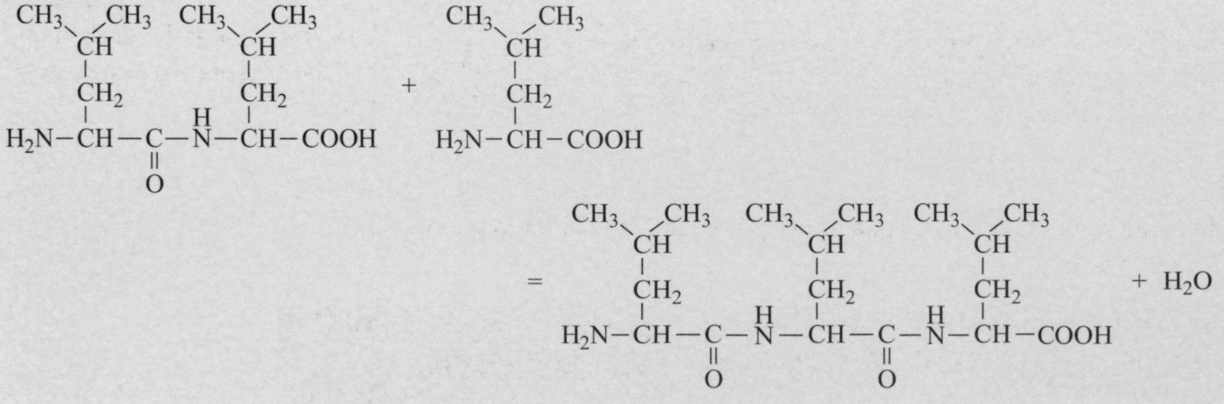

(3.6)

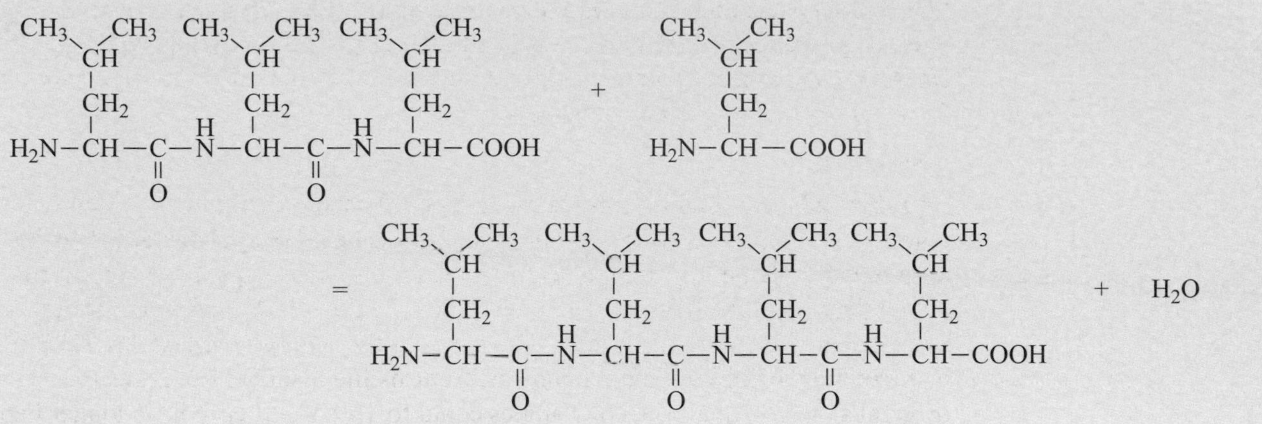

$$CH_3\underset{\underset{\underset{\underset{H_2N-CH-C}{||}}{CH_2}}{CH}}{\diagdown}CH_3 \quad ... \quad (3.7)$$

(3.7)

## Question 3.2

Ethanol has a relatively high boiling temperature because it is able to form hydrogen bonds between OH groups on adjacent molecules throughout the liquid. These are relatively strong and require a considerable input of energy (latent heat of evaporation) to break them so that the liquid ethanol can turn into gas; so the boiling temperature is high.

Propane cannot form hydrogen bonds. It is non-polar, so can only form London forces. As propane molecules are small the London forces are very weak. They are easily broken, so the boiling temperature is low.

(Note that propane and ethanol molecules are roughly the same size, so ethanol will also have London forces of attraction between its molecules. However, these are very weak for small molecules, compared with hydrogen bonds, so can be disregarded.)

## Question 3.3

Figure 3.16 shows the possibility of hydrogen bonding between the OH groups in parts of two segments of the protein. Figure 3.17 shows the possible formation of a sulfur–sulfur bond (disulfide link). There is also the possibility of London forces between the hydrocarbon chains.

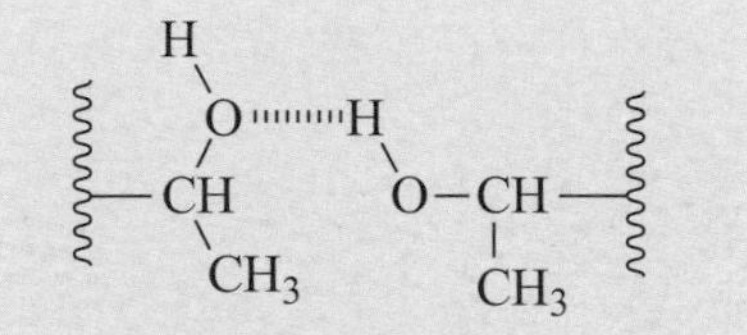

**Figure 3.16** Hydrogen bonding; the protein backbone is shown as a wiggly line.

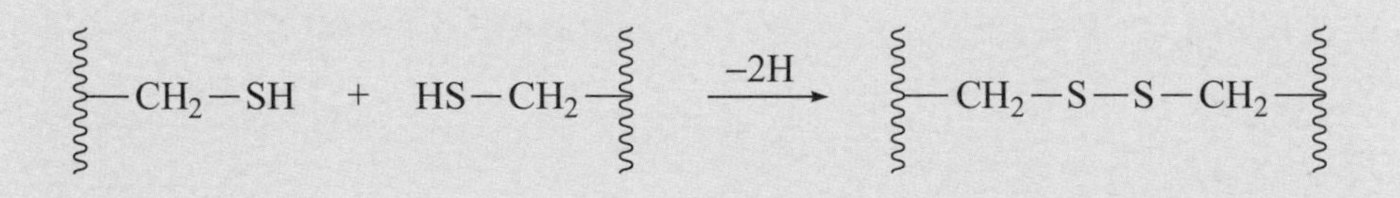

**Figure 3.17** Sulfur–sulfur bond formation; the protein backbone is shown as a wiggly line.

## Question 3.4

A molecule of arachidonic acid consists of a long hydrocarbon chain terminating in a carboxylic acid group, **3.7**.

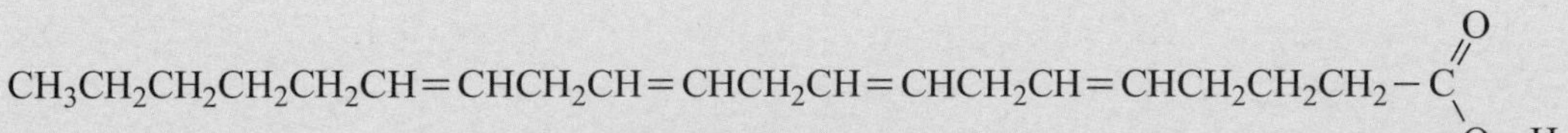

$$CH_3CH_2CH_2CH_2CH_2CH=CHCH_2CH=CHCH_2CH=CHCH_2CH=CHCH_2CH_2CH_2-C\underset{O-H}{\overset{O}{\diagup}}$$

**3.7 arachidonic acid**

The hydrocarbon chain is non-polar and can form London forces to hydrocarbon chains on other molecules, e.g. to groups such as a $-CH_2-$ chain, **3.8**, or a benzene ring, **3.9**.

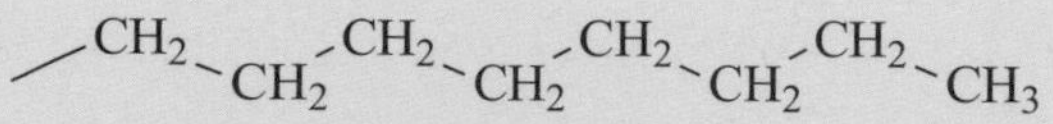

**3.8**

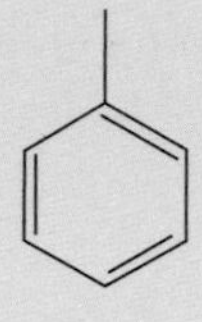

**3.9**

Because the hydrocarbon chain is long, the London forces would be quite strong.

The carboxylic acid group could form hydrogen bonds to a variety of polar groups on other molecules, as shown in Figure 3.18; for example to alcohols (a), an amine (b), an ester (c) or an amide (d). It could also form hydrogen bonds to other carboxylic acids.

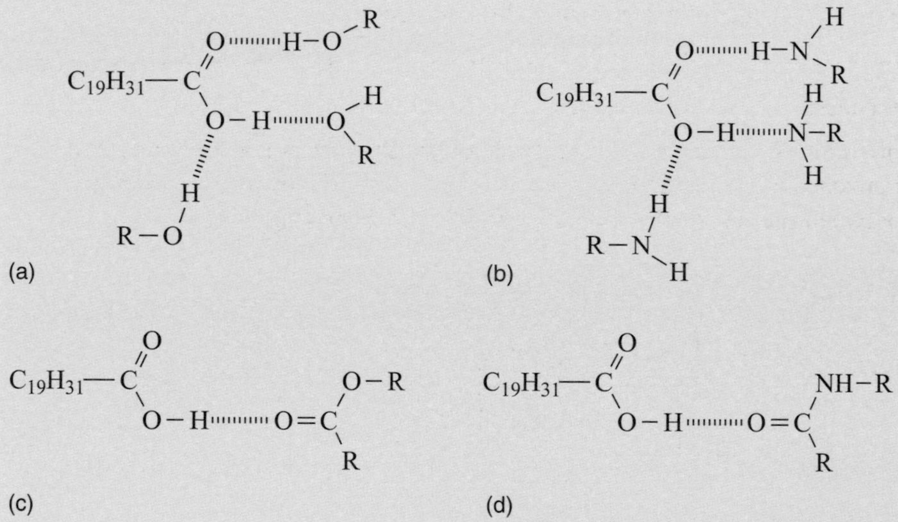

**Figure 3.18**   Hydrogen bonds between the carboxylic acid group of arachidonic acid and polar groups of other molecules. Note that the R groups can vary.

**Question 4.1**
Two molecules of water are needed on the left-hand side of the equation because there are two ester groups to be hydrolysed on each molecule of cocaine. (Strictly speaking these should have been shown in Reaction 4.1, but chemists often miss out minor parts of equations when they think their identity is obvious; this is why we use ⟶ and not = here.)

## Question 4.2

Your models should clearly show that the blue nitrogen and red oxygen atom centres representing compound **4.8** can be overlapped with those of cocaine, whereas those in the model representing compound **4.7** cannot. The distance between the nitrogen and oxygen centres is shorter in **4.7** than in cocaine. So, we would expect **4.8** to be the better local anaesthetic.

The greater distance between the nitrogen atom and the ester in the *trans* isomer **4.8** (see Section 2.6) makes it a good fit, whilst the *cis* isomer **4.7** has the nitrogen atom and the ester too close to match onto the nitrogen and ester of cocaine. So, in this instance, the *trans* isomer can be expected to be more effective as a local anaesthetic than the *cis* isomer.

## Question 4.3

A property of a carbon–carbon double bond is that it prevents rotation, relative to each other, of the two atoms that it joins (see Section 2.6). This keeps the distance between the oxygen atom of the ester group and the nitrogen atom of the amine group different in Figures 4.12 and 4.13.

## Question 4.4

Similarities:

* an amine nitrogen atom in identical structural environments, bonded to two ethyl ($CH_3CH_2-$) groups and a $-CH_2-$, at one end of the molecule;

* a benzene ring at the other end of the molecule;

* the amine nitrogen separated by two spacer groups from an atom of oxygen.

Differences:

* procaine, **4.5**, has an ester group between the rest of the molecule and the benzene ring whereas lidocaine, **4.9**, has an amide group (see margin) between the rest of the molecule and the benzene ring;

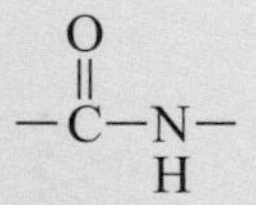

amide group

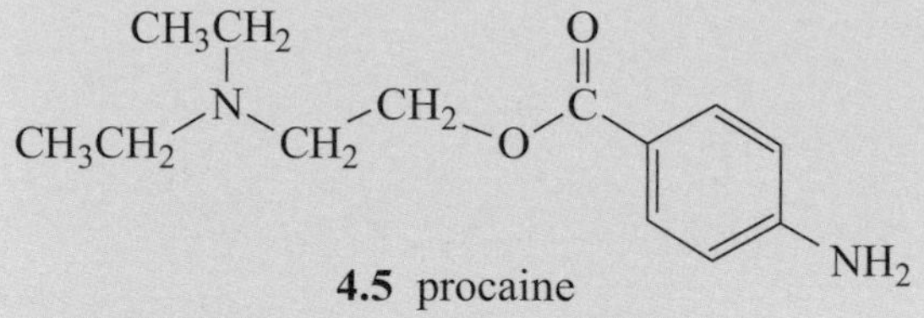

**4.5** procaine

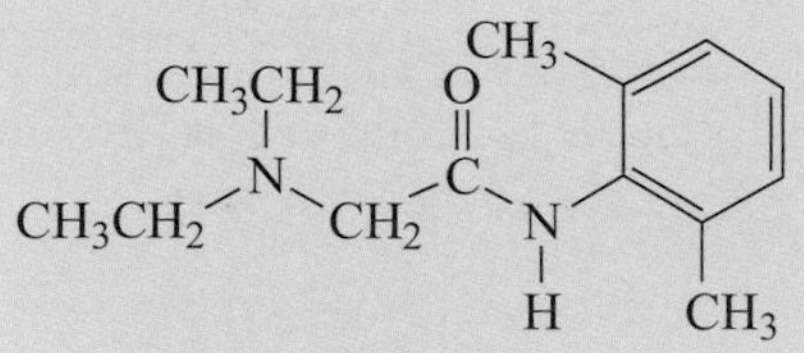

**4.9** lidocaine

* procaine has four spacer groups or atoms (so five bonds) between the amine nitrogen and the benzene ring; lidocaine has three spacer groups or atoms (so four bonds) between the amine nitrogen and the benzene ring;

* the other groups substituted on the benzene ring are different for each of the molecules.

**159**

Important features that influence the anaesthetic effect of lidocaine and procaine:

- it seems likely that the amine nitrogen and its structural environment may be important, as they are identical in the molecules;
- if the benzene ring is important in the binding of the molecules, it appears that its exact distance from the amine nitrogen is not important;
- the other substituent groups on the benzene ring do not appear to be important;
- the partial models can be manipulated so that the distance between the amine nitrogen atom and the oxygen atom are the same. This could be an important feature, but the exact nature of the spacer groups between them does not appear to be important.

**Question 4.5**

There is no single correct answer to this question. The important thing is the sequence of events involved in the strategy for the development of lidocaine. An acceptable answer would include steps 1–9:

1   Isolation of cocaine from coca leaves. (Done by Albert Niemann in 1860.)
2   Testing to confirm its properties. (Done experimentally by Sigmund Freud and Carl Koller.)
3   Determination of molecular structure. (It is interesting that, historically, cocaine's complete molecular structure was not determined before attempts were made to make improved anaesthetics, but some features of the structure were known.)
4   Determination of which molecular features are responsible for activity. Even though cocaine's full structure was not known, essential features of it could be identified. Synthesis of new, related compounds.
5   Testing new compounds.
6   Identification of molecular features responsible for activity led to amylocaine and procaine.
7   Further related compounds prepared.
8   Testing.
9   Further development led to lidocaine.

No doubt the synthesis of further related compounds, followed by testing, will produce more local anaesthetics over time.

**Question 5.1**

Your structure should look like N≡N, or a model with three of the longer bonds joining two nitrogen atoms.

(a) As the two atoms are identical it follows that there are no permanent dipoles in the molecule. There will be temporary dipoles, though, so nitrogen molecules are able to attract other molecules only by London forces. These are weak because nitrogen is a small molecule (see Section 3.2.4).

(b) Because it can only form weak intermolecular bonds, nitrogen has limited solubility in a polar solvent such as water. To get enough nitrogen dissolved in the blood to cause nitrogen narcosis a high pressure is needed, so this is only a problem with deep diving.

## Question 5.2

Enzymes and receptors are globular proteins. You should recall from Section 3.2 that parts of the chains are tied to other parts by a variety of intramolecular bonds and attractions; ionic attractions, disulfide links, hydrogen bonds, dipole–dipole attractions and London forces. As the primary structure of each chain of a particular globular protein is identical to all the other chains of that protein, the intramolecular attractions are also identical and hold each molecule in exactly the same shape. There is much less scope for intramolecular attractions in the chains comprising only $-CH_2-$ groups. The chains are non-polar, so only relatively weak London forces will be present; the chains do not adopt a common shape in each molecule because there are no specific points, identical in each molecule, where strong intramolecular attractions (e.g. hydrogen bonds) can form.

## Question 5.3

See Reaction 5.2. Note: the suxamethonium molecule is shown in this shape for convenience. You may have drawn it as a straight line and this, or any other shape, is perfectly correct (see Activity 1.2 and Question 1.1).

(5.2)

## Question 5.4

The active compound in curare is tubocurarine (Figure 5.10). There is no mechanism for its removal because the tubocurarine molecule does not contain any ester groups; therefore acetylcholinesterase cannot catalyse its hydrolysis.

## Question 6.1

Two such compounds are **6.20** and **6.21**; these compounds are identical to adrenalin except that in each case a hydrogen atom (marked in red) has been used to replace one of the two OH groups attached to the benzene ring.

Although not required as an answer to the question, it is interesting to note that compound **6.20** has no biological activity, and compound **6.21** has no anti-asthmatic activity. So, it would appear that both groups in conjunction are necessary for a compound to have anti-asthmatic activity.

## Question 6.2

You should note that each of the structures has the two functional groups that can potentially bind to both sites. It is the distance represented by the number of bonds between them that is important. Compound **6.14** can only fit one of the sites; compound **6.15** will fit one of the sites, and will almost fit the second site; compound **6.16** fits both sites.

**6.20**

**6.21**

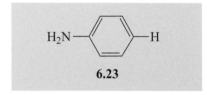

**6.22**

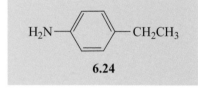

**6.23**

**6.24**

**Question 6.3**

(a) Structure **6.22** is probably the molecule with the simplest structure that can bind to both sites of the receptor.

The molecule containing only two carbons in the chain $HS—CH_2—CH_2—NH_2$ is unable to span the distance between the binding sites.

(b) Compound **6.17** can be arranged to fit the two sites in Figure 6.15 but **6.18** cannot. The shortest carbon chain between the SH and $NH_2$ groups contains four carbon atoms in both cases. However, the carbon chain of **6.17** is flexible and can twist so that the groups take up the correct positions in space but the benzene ring of **6.18** has no flexibility so the $—NH_2$ and $—SH$ groups can't take the orientation required to fit the receptor site.

**Question 6.4**

Two possible compounds are **6.23** and **6.24**. In **6.23** the oxygen-containing $—OCH_3$ group has been removed and replaced by an $—H$ atom. In **6.24** a smaller modification is made in that the $CH_3—$ group remains but the $—O—$ atom has been replaced by $—CH_2—$.

**Question 7.1**

Unfortunately the peptides from snake venom, like the proteins in food, are readily broken down by digestive enzymes present in the stomach. So if other drugs can be developed that can be taken orally, these will be preferred.

**Question 7.2**

Because the carboxylic acid group has lost a hydrogen ion ($H^+$), it is left with a negative charge. The group on ACE that binds to this, therefore needs to be positively charged. An example of this would be $–NH_3^+$, see Figure 3.11.

**Question 7.3**

After a heart attack, some of the heart muscle is damaged and weakened. This makes it more difficult for the heart to pump blood. Captopril helps slow down any further weakening of the heart, by lowering blood pressure and hence reducing the physical demands on the heart muscle.

**Question 8.1**

Of the three structures, only (a), the sulfonium chloride, would have antibacterial properties. The molecule has a water-soluble cationic group at one end and the rest of the structure is a long non-polar hydrocarbon chain, able to form London forces to non-polar parts of other molecules. It is therefore able to replace the phospholipids in the cell membrane. (b) The alkylbenzene sulfonate has an anionic (negatively charged) end to the chain so it is unable to mimic the phospholipids in the cell membrane and replace them. (c) is just a long non-polar chain and lacks any water-soluble part at either end so, again, is unable to replace phospholipids.

**Question 8.2**

The $—OH$ group does not appear to be attached to the benzene ring. There needs to be a bond shown between the oxygen atom and one of the carbon atoms in the ring. Also, there is no attempt to show any representation of the three double bonds in the ring.

**Question 8.3**

There are several possibilities.

The hydrogen atom of the phenol's —OH group could form a hydrogen bond to almost any oxygen or nitrogen atom in the cell protein, so likely groups would be alcohols (—OH), amines (—NH$_2$) and amides (—NH—CO—). Other possibilities would be carboxylic acids (—COOH) and esters (—COOR).

The oxygen atom of the phenol's —OH group needs a hydrogen atom joined to either oxygen or nitrogen to hydrogen bond to. So, likely groups here would be any of the above, except esters.

**Question 8.4**

The molecule of eugenol contains a benzene ring attached to an —OH group, so it is a phenol. When a phenol also has a longer hydrocarbon chain on the ring its antiseptic properties are improved so eugenol, with a side-chain of —CH$_2$—CH=CH$_2$, should have antiseptic properties.

[You may know of the traditional use of cloves to alleviated toothache. Oil of cloves is also a mild local anaesthetic, so has a numbing effect on the tooth when a clove is crushed against it. Maybe the awful taste acts to take one's mind off the toothache as well! Certainly there is no harm in flooding the infected area with an antibacterial, though.]

**Question 8.5**

If clavulanic acid was always mixed with penicillin before use, there is an increased chance that bacteria would evolve a mechanism to avoid its effect, thereby remaining unaffected by the future use of antibiotics containing penicillin and clavulanic acid.

**Question 8.6**

(a) The deactivation of β-lactamase by clavulanic acid is shown in Reaction 8.3.

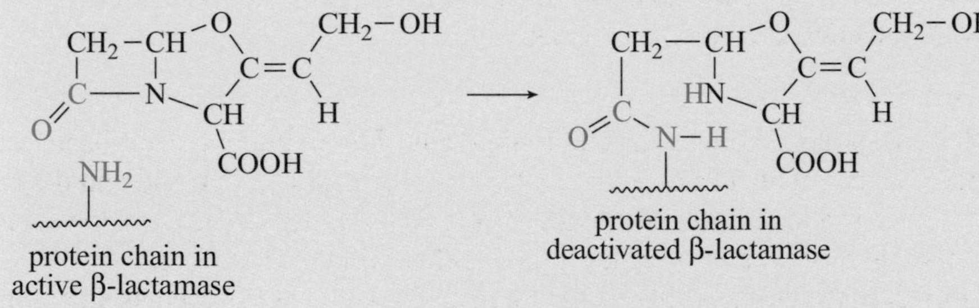

(b) It is an amide. The colour coding in Reaction 8.3 should help you to trace the atoms involved in the reaction.

(c) As the side-chain on the 4-membered ring of penicillin appears to be important in determining its activity, it is likely that the absence of such a side-chain in clavulanic acid is responsible for its lack of activity.

### Question 8.7

Reaction 8.4 shows the other product formed which has a benzene ring with three of its hydrogen atoms substituted by amine groups.

$$+ 4H \longrightarrow \tag{8.4}$$

### Question 9.1

The influenza virus seems to have an unusual ability, even among viruses, to mutate quickly to give different strains. Each strain differs to a greater or lesser extent in the proteins that are the key to the action of the virus. As a result, it is very difficult to find molecules that are active against all strains.

### Question 9.2

Sialidase has a particular function in releasing replicated influenza virus particles to allow them to propagate the disease. The natural substrate in the host cell is bound sialic acid that is cleaved as part of this process. If a molecule that acts as a sialidase inhibitor is present, then by the definition of an inhibitor, it will bind to the enzyme without itself being changed. Once bound, it prevents the sialic acid from having access to the sialidase receptor, and so interferes with replication of the virus.

### Question 9.3

Both structures have a six-membered ring containing one C=C double bond. There is a difference in that oseltamivir only has carbon atoms in the ring, but zanamivir has five carbons and one oxygen in the ring.

### Question 9.4

The first step would be to isolate the enzyme ACE, and to produce crystals for X-ray crystallography. This in itself is no easy task. Once crystals are available, the structure of the enzyme can be determined from a combination of the X-ray data and knowledge of the amino acid sequence in the enzyme obtained from separate measurements. To see how captopril binds to the ACE receptor, an X-ray study of an ACE crystal soaked in a solution of the captopril inhibitor would be highly advantageous. Once the ACE structure had been determined, GRID calculations would provide an indication of the various 'hot spots' for different types of probe groups. Finally, careful examination of the binding site would see if there is (a) unoccupied space in the receptor and (b) suitably placed functional groups that could interact with additional groups added to the captopril template. New molecular structures could then be designed and synthesised. Tests *in vitro* and *in vivo* would then follow to see if the predictions are borne out in practice, followed by pre-clinical and clinical testing. (We have just spent several hundred million pounds of the pharmaceutical company's budget!)

**Question 9.5**

It is less likely that significant improvement in activity would be possible than in the case of the sialidase inhibitor. The lead compound in the latter case was only weakly active *in vitro*, inactive *in vivo*, and not very selective, so there was a lot of room for improvement. In contrast, captopril is an existing drug and is highly active and very specific. It would seem that there is less scope for improvement in this case.

# Acknowledgements

The Course Team acknowledges the contribution of Yvonne Ashmore in advising on and producing the chemical structures for the course.

Grateful acknowledgement is made to the following sources for permission to reproduce material within this book.

*Cover image*: David Mack/Science Photo Library; *Figure 1.2*: Sydney Hoff/ The New Yorker, 28 September 1957; *Figure 3.6*: Center for Structural Biology, Yale University; *Figure 3.15*: Professor A. Malcolm Campbell, Davidson College, North Carolina, USA; *Figure 4.1*: Dr Morley Read/Science Photo Library; *Figures 4.2 and 4.4*: The Advertising Archives; *Figure 4.3*: Walter H. Hodge/Peter Arnold Inc. New York; *Figure 6.1*: Jerry Mason/Science Photo Library; *Figure 7.1a*: Courtesy of Cambridge Botanical Gardens; *Figure 8.3*: Photograph courtesy of Wellcome Library, London. Image of stamp courtesy of The British Postal Museum and Archive (BPMA); *Figure 8.13*: St Mary's Hospital Medical School/Science Photo Library; *Figure 8.16*: Hoechst Ltd; *Figure 8.17*: Steve Allen/Science Photo Library; *Figure 8.18*: Ciba-Geigy Ltd; *Figure 9.1*: Alfred Pasieka/Science Photo Library; *Figure 9.3*: NIBSC/Science Photo Library; *Figure 9.4*: Kaplan, M.M. and Webster, R.G. 'The epidemiology of influenza', *Scientific American*, Vol. 237, No. 6, December 1977, Scientific American Inc., copyright © Bunji Tagawa; *Figure 9.7*: von Itzstein, M. et al. (1993) 'Rational design of potent sialidase-based inhibitors of influenza virus replication', *Nature*, Vol. 363, copyright © Nature Publishing Group; *Figure 10.1a*: Scott Camazine/Science Photo Library; *Figure 10.1b*: Peter Arnold Inc/Still Pictures.

# Index

Page numbers in *italics* refer to items mainly in figures or tables.